Marty Hill has written a practical a
us backstage into an often unseen,
of the church. As one who interacts with Marty on a weekly basis,
and as one who depends on Marty, and others like him, I commend
his words and example to you.

— **Max Lucado, Pastor and Bestselling Author**

When you happen upon a gemstone you want to tell everyone
about it. To know Marty, his heart for ministry and his pursuit
of excellence, is a blessing and an inspiration. To glean from his
knowledge and experience is a real treasure that would otherwise
take a lifetime to learn. Having worked with Marty for nearly ten
years in worship ministry, the lessons and information he offers
are trustworthy and invaluable. For those who truly desire to have
a ministry through media this book is a must read.

— **Dave Hill, Pastor of Worship and Arts,**
Graceview Baptist Church, Burleson, Texas

I worked with Marty Hill for over a dozen years at the church I
pastored in the Dallas/Fort Worth area. When the opportunity
arose for me to bring Marty to San Antonio at the church I served
for the last nine years, I took it and thankfully he said yes. Marty
is a living, breathing example of the message he has penned here.
He is a minister, a manager and a Master of Technology. And, he
has certainly seen thousands of lives changed. Technology done
right moves hearts and multiplies the message to millions. I highly
recommend this tool to anyone who carries the awesome kingdom
responsibility of using technology to raise up the name of Jesus.

— **Randy Frazee, Pastor & Author of**
What Happens After You Die
www. randyfrazee.com

The Professional's Guide to Technical Ministry is a thoughtful go-to-guide toward a well-rounded understanding of technology in the church. Have you ever wondered how technology can be leveraged to help change lives for the better? Marty Hill shares compelling observations for church leaders who crave clarity on the effective use of technology in the church.

— **Gerry True**
Communication Arts Minister
Oak Hills Church
San Antonio, Texas

In *The Professional's Guide to Technical Ministry* Marty shows that he has been formed by God as well as by the ups and downs of technical ministry. In this book he offers a godly and professional approach to a ministry often misunderstood by pastors and church leaders. Rather than telling those in technical ministry how to be more technical, he them offers a path of Christian formation for working with and for pastors, lay leaders, and volunteers. By keeping the cart before the horse, this book will center the life of a paid or unpaid technical leader for ministry—and this makes all the difference. And, there is plenty of technical advice and tools to help move a church's technical ministry forward and into the future.

— **Scott D. Campbell**
Woodmoor Campus Pastor,
The Ascent Church Monument, Colorado
www.theascentchurch.com

Marty Hill knows what he's talking about when it comes to the media tech support ministries need today. Having worked with him, I know that he is a seasoned professional with a ministry heart and a great sense of humor. Read what he writes and then invite him to brief your media team or speak at your conference.

— Dr. Ron Jones, Lead Pastor,
Atlantic Shores Baptist Church, Virginia Beach
President and Lead Bible Teacher,
Something Good Radio
www.somethinggoodradio.org

Clear. Comprehensive. Detailed. Descriptive. Whether a ministry is dabbling in the early stages of technical media or employing a large staff in a highly complicated worship expression, Marty Hill has provided a powerful guide for any ministry looking to take their technical ministry to the next level.

— Tom Anthony
Minister of Community Life, Oak Hills Church
San Antonio, Texas
Founder of the Neighborhood Collective
www.neighborhoodcollective.org

THE PROFESSIONAL'S GUIDE TO

TECHNICAL MINISTRY

THE PROFESSIONAL'S GUIDE TO TECHNICAL MINISTRY

How Your Work as a Minister, Manager, and
Master of Technology Can Change Lives
Copyright © 2017 Marty Hill
Published by Quaddot Productions

Edited by Blake Atwood
Cover Design by MartinPublishingServices.com
Author Photo by Miriam Thomas, themiruamtraci.com

Section Photos
Minister Section Photo
Image licensed through Shutterstock.com by Marty Hill and Quaddot Productions.
Used by Permission.
Manager Section & Master Of Technology Photos
Image licensed through Stockphotos.com by Marty Hill and Quaddot Productions.
Used by Permission.

Marty Hill is available for speaking engagements as well as consulting.
www.marty-hill.com

THE PROFESSIONAL'S GUIDE TO

TECHNICAL MINISTRY

How Your Work as a Minister, Manager, and Master of Technology Can Change Lives

MARTY HILL

Thank you to my wife, Lavonne, who has been a
positive, driving force behind me throughout
this the entire process of creating and producing
this book. Thanks for keeping me focused and
for your constant encouragement!
I could not have done this without you!

This book is dedicated to Nadine Branson Reed,
the best Mother-in-Law anyone could
ever hope to have.

CONTENTS

BEYOND MEDIA 101 AND 201

Is that what it's really all about?

In one of the Pinky and the Brain cartoon episodes, when Brain, as he did in every episode, asks Pinky if he is pondering what he is pondering, Pinky replies, "I think so, Brain. But suppose we do the hokey pokey and turn ourselves around, is that what it's really all about?"

How many times have you searched for new ideas on what is next in technical ministry only to find more and more sources on why your church needs one? Or how to start one? Or many other beginning topics?

In our technical ministry world, just as Pinky noticed with the hokey pokey, that's NOT what it is all about.

If conferences and seminars were college classes, how to begin a technical ministry would be Media 101 and how to setup and maintain these systems would be Media 201. While these are important and valuable to the ministry in that stage, for those of us who have been doing this for a while, these sometimes frustrate and make some feel alone. If you believe you and your ministry are beyond Media 101 and 201, then this book might be for you.

It does not matter if you are not a huge mega-church with seemingly an unlimited budget, a huge paid tech staff and an army of volunteers who work during the week at the local major network television affiliate. There are many things you can do to take your ministry to new levels. We can only cover some of them in the scope of this book. Our ministry is always growing and changing. Thanks to people like you who are always looking for new ways to grow, ideas and concepts presented here can lead to new ones.

This book assumes you and your church have been doing this for a while, but are now inspired to find out what is next.

We will discuss topics such as IMAG and video storytelling and will go pretty deep into volunteer management. We will even go into harder topics such as working with pastors and other ministry leaders, managing work and family time, etc. We will talk about how to be confident and sure in knowledge but demonstrate attitudes of servanthood and humility. We will also look at different job descriptions and the importance of planning backup systems before we jump into current trends in church media and possibilities for the future. Along with the trends and future possibilities, we will discuss how changes in church media can positively and/or negatively affect the congregation.

Finally, there are links and other resources provided that will help you with practical matters in your tech ministry. While going into detail on these subjects is behind the scope of this book, I hope by providing you with further resources will assist you in the management of your media ministry.

> ## Strive to be resourceful,
> ## not just resourced.

Allow me to chase a rabbit here. All of these resources are only here because somebody else thought of them. I encourage you to be creative. There is no law that says you cannot be the innovator, the person who envisions the next new normal. Use these resources as benchmarks or as tools to get through some times where you need solutions where it is not coming to you. Maybe there are ideas included you haven't considered. Regardless, strive to be resourceful, not just resourced. To be cliché, think outside the box!

"Wabbit" chasing done, application of the principles and skills in this book enables us to become better leaders of our ministries. The better we lead, the happier our team and the better our technical ministries function. Then our role in worship services becomes more valuable because we support the worship experience with minimal to no distraction. In the end, we are there to serve, and I pray the contents of this book will work to assist you and your ministry in a very fulfilling and rewarding way.

While we are looking for what is next in technical ministry, and wondering if what we've found is "what it's all about," I'm reminded of what should be the overall inspiration of why we do what we do.

A.W. Tozer summed this up brilliantly with his quote,

> "We are saved to worship God. All that Christ has done in the past and all that He is doing now leads to this one end."[1]

Let us not ever forget to worship the creator of everything we use as tools of our ministry and not have our focus be on those tools. An expression from a few years back used regarding Christian dating, but applies here,

> "Worship the creator,
> not His creation!"

---

1   http://www.goodreads.com/quotes/442775-we-are-saved-to-worship-god-all-that-christ-has

MINISTER

CHAPTER 1
Knowledge and Humility

The Three Stooges weren't plumbers, but that didn't stop them from trying to emulate such professionals in the 1940 episode, "A Plumbing We Will Go." Because they needed to escape from the police, Larry, Moe, and Curly jump into a nearby vehicle emblazoned with "Casey the Plumber." To continue their ruse, they have to prove their mettle as plumbers.

Their first problem—which should have been evidence of their ignorance—was a failure to turn off the water before beginning work. For most of the episode, water flies everywhere. Curly adds a pipe to stop a leak, peers at it to make sure the leak's fixed, then turns around to see water pouring out of the pipe's other end. So he adds another pipe, and another, and another until he's trapped himself in a web of pipes.

Meanwhile, Moe is working on pipes beneath the floor occupied by Curly. As Moe twists and turns the leaking pipes, he offers the only rational explanation he can devise for why so much water is pouring out: "All these pipes are full of termites!" Later, the Three Stooges find pipes containing wires. Knowing no better, they remove the wires and connect them to the water lines as well, which results in water pouring out of the homeowners' telephone and stove!

Moe's quip during his battle against the never-ending flow of water reveals his assumptions and his ignorance: "Just goes to show ya, you don't have to have brains to be a plumber." It's humorous because the audience knows you do have to have brains to be a plumber. Obviously, this is why the Three Stooges are having such difficulty. In fact, the Stooges built their show around such ignorance.

The plot of nearly all of their episodes relied on their inexperience or ignorance and their ability to convince people otherwise, who would then be exasperated by their total and complete incompetence by the end of the show.

That's hilarious for an audience, but it's not so funny in the real world.

> "Remember, with great power comes great responsibility."[2]

The Necessity of Knowledge

Knowledge in technical ministry is a must. You cannot act as a technical minster like the Stooges acted like plumbers. You

---

2   *Uncle Ben, Spiderman (2002) Columbia Pictures Corporation Marvel Enterprises*

must have the knowledge (or at least the drive to seek the knowledge) of what technical ministry requires. This book should help you in that endeavor.

You cannot lead a team of volunteers without technical knowledge. You may be able to wing it for a while and rely on your volunteers, but I'd hazard a guess that your job might soon be in jeopardy if that's your standard operating procedure. Plus, knowledge commands respect. When a volunteer knows that you have the skills to develop efficient systems and the ability to train them, they will respond positively to your requests to help out.

Without the right knowledge, you cannot navigate an inevitable crisis or even the weekly demands that church jobs uniquely place upon a technical minister's shoulders. Knowledge is such an instrumental part of this job that it almost doesn't merit discussion. But it's not our knowledge that I'm chiefly worried about; rather, it's the other side of having specialized knowledge that we must grapple with.

With Great Knowledge Comes Great...Arrogance

The problem with people who know a lot, and know that they know a lot, is that they can lean toward an attitude of arrogance. Such people must be the resident expert and constantly acknowledged as such. They have all the answers and rarely consider others' ideas and viewpoints.

This is pride, and, believe it not, the Bible has much to say about that original sin:

> *"Pride goes before destruction,*
> *and a haughty spirit before a fall,"*
>
> *Proverbs 16:18*

> *"When pride comes, then comes disgrace,*
> *but with the humble is wisdom."*
>
> *Proverbs 11:2*

The author of the devotional Our Daily Bread wrote,

> "Pride is the only disease known to man that makes everyone sick except the one who has it."

Abraham Lincoln once said,

> "What kills a skunk is the publicity it gives itself."

Ultimately, feeling high about yourself will eventually bring you low.

Technical ministry isn't exempt from such know-it-alls. In fact, because we have such specialized knowledge, and often over a broad range of topics that most other people on the church staff have little understanding about, we may be the most prone to arrogance on account of competence.

It's okay to secretly believe yourself to be the most experienced and knowledgeable person about technology in your ministry, but it's another thing to wear your pride. Ministry has no place for pride and arrogance. If it's present, then your leaders, volunteers, and congregation will soon learn of it. So long as you flaunt your knowledge and demand respect for your abilities, your stay at that ministry, or any other, will be on borrowed time.

Five Ways to Release Your Pride

Unfortunately, pride isn't something that can simply be done away with once and for all. Pride will rear its head over and over again in your life and especially in your professional calling as a minister. The enemy uses his earliest tactic because he knows how divisive pride can be to relationships. And while we may think our job is about pushing buttons and sending emails, our job is more foundational about people. It is really the following:

> We are not **Technical** Ministers.
> We are Technical **Ministers**.

In other words, we all wrestle with this, and I believe that we can all benefit from the following steps to help rid ourselves of a prideful demeanor.

1. Admit the problem to God, yourself, and a trusted person.

To fix a problem, you have to admit that you have a problem. Spend time in prayer allowing God to kindly show you where you may be exuding pride. Ask for forgiveness. Plead for a changed heart in that respect. Admit to yourself that you have a problem and try to become more aware of the moments in which pride sneaks up on you like a silent serpent. Consider telling your spouse, a close friend, or even someone you work with about your decision to consciously fight against your pride. Let them be your encouragement and your accountability.

2. Model the Apostle Paul's humility.

Aside from Jesus, I don't think anyone else has as much merit as Paul to think highly of himself. He wrote half of the New Testament and was instrumental in the birth of the early church. (What have you done today?) So it's shocking to read what he wrote about himself during the time in which God was using him to alter the course of history:

> "For I am the least of the apostles,
> unworthy to be called an apostle"
>
> 1 Corinthians 15:9

"To me, though I am the very least of all the saints, this grace was given, to preach to the Gentiles the unsearchable riches of Christ"

Ephesians 3:8

"The saying is trustworthy and deserving of full acceptance, that Christ Jesus came into the world to save sinners, of whom I am the foremost"

1 Timothy 1:15

Of course, Paul is simply modeling his humility on the ultimate example of humility, Jesus, who

"...humbled himself by becoming obedient to the point of death, even death on a cross"

Philippians 2:8

Humility is a modest opinion of oneself: in your abilities, your station in life, etc. The humble do not promote themselves. It's one thing to seek advancement in your career, but it's another thing to wear it on your sleeve and boast about your skills, ensuring everyone knows how great you are. Some will argue that if they don't bring attention to themselves, nobody else will. That's not true. (Or maybe a prideful person's skills aren't quite as good as they think they are!)

Remember:

"Humble yourselves before the Lord,
and he will exalt you"

James 4:10

Humility is the foundation for the next three ways to release your pride. Without humility, you will not be able to authentically follow these next three recommendations, which are all closely linked.

The humble do not promote themselves.

3. Listen.

A pastor or director can listen to the suggestions of a staff member lower in the food chain and opt not to take their recommendation. However, after time passes, that leader may decide that the suggestion was actually a good idea. They'll present it to the rest of the team for feedback or implementation. But the problem is that time has passed and people are forgetful—and prideful.

"Don't worry, the team is totally open to new ideas."

Image licensed through Stockphotos.com by Marty Hill and Quaddot Productions.
Used by Permission.

If the leader fails to mention where "their" bright idea originated, their new idea will make then look like the great leader everyone else believes them to be. Whether the leader intentionally meant to forget that someone else had first suggested the idea or not doesn't matter because the result will be identical: the lack of respect given to the less experienced staff member will hurt and simmer in their heart. And very likely, they won't speak up about it. Their love and graciousness for God, their church, their leader, and their team may keep them from admitting to being hurt. Such a prideful act on the leader's part will inevitably lead to strained relationships, which is why it may be a good idea to check in with seemingly quiet or disgruntled staffers and simply ask, "Have I been listening to you lately?"

Better listening leads to higher respect and greater humility. When you listen well, you're more prone to enact the last two steps toward becoming a more humble technical ministry leader.

4. Give credit where credit is due.

If your technical ministry career has been anything like mine, there's a good chance that you've been the only paid technical staffer. Consequently, volunteers have likely been a huge part of your team. (Later chapters will cover working with volunteers in depth.) Though you're very thankful for their help, you understand that they can't always help you on the schedule that would be most beneficial to you. So, what volunteers aren't able to do often falls back into your lap.

In other words, you feel a deep ownership of the technical ministry of your church. So what's your natural response when someone says, "Great job on that video!" or "Those graphics were incredible"? Even if it's just a quick "Thank you," such a reply evidences a personal thanks and not a communal thanks.

> Humility is an essential virtue
> for successful ministry leaders.

Our go-to reply to such successes ought to be, "Well, we have a great team!" When and where credit is due, pass it on. If a specific person or team of people worked on that project, name the people in your thanks. Ensure that the people in your church, from the leadership to those in the pews, know that the technical ministry is not a one-person show. Giving credit has a corollary though, and this single act of humility might be the most difficult.

5. Take blame.

When things don't go well, take the heat. If the lyrics mismatch the music, the light cues go haywire, or every microphone has a dead battery—it's your fault. When your superiors ask you what happened, you should say, "My fault. It won't happen again."

Then go to your team with a nonjudgmental teaching moment. Don't pass along negatives in a negative fashion. You are your team's leader. Take the fall when things fail, but let your team have the glory when things go well. This demonstrates the kind of humility you want to emphasize to your team. And don't be prideful about your humility: your blame-taking doesn't need to be pointed out. Your team (and likely your staff) will pick up on it.

Smart people serve on tech teams! Their success is your success. They might get the glory, but you will receive their respect and admiration of being a great leader.

Personally, I believe that humility is an essential virtue for successful ministry leaders. This isn't something you brag about to others. Rather, you consistently work on it in your life and pray for God's guidance as you go. It is a character trait that is more difficult for some than for others and must be studied and mined, privately, between yourself and God. There is no other way. To do overtly is to undermine and defeat the entire concept.

When I was a freshman in college in the late 1970's in Denton, TX, I heard the pastor at Highland Baptist Church, Rev. Jimmy Stiles, say something I've never forgotten. Even though today he wouldn't know me from Adam, his comment from the pulpit that Sunday during one of his sermons impacted my life. His observation was simply,

> "Humility is the one thing you can have, but the first time you admit to having it, you no longer do."

Thinking that through, therefore, humility can only be practiced by you. When humility has become an integral part of who you are, it will be noticed by others.

And because I'm a technical minister, I like to boil my thoughts down to easily memorable equations:

Knowledge - Humility =
Arrogance and a short ministry tenure

Knowledge + Humility =
A long ministry tenure with the Lord's rewards

Allow this passage to be your guiding verses when it comes to increasing your technical knowledge while also strengthening your humility:

"Do nothing from selfish ambition or conceit, but in humility count others more significant than yourselves. Let each of you look not only to his own interests, but also to the interests of others."

Philippians 2:3–4

Before finishing this discussion on humility, there's one more issue I feel a need to speak into, and it's one that seems somewhat unique to technical ministry.

Are You an Amateur or a Professional?

This question is spawned from a personal pet peeve. It's a soapbox I jump onto every once in a while. When contemplating this book, I was convicted that maybe, just maybe, if I felt this way then others may too.

How you handle pet peeves and soapboxes has to be carefully considered because you don't want to hurt your growing virtues of humility and servanthood. But practicing humility doesn't mean that you can't stand up for yourself when your integrity is directly or indirectly criticized. This is where your dependence on the Holy Spirit will guide you. Sometimes, the solution is just to let an issue pass. At other times, you'll want to confront the problem lovingly.

This topic may seem to contradict the previous discussion of humility. However, I believe that the better these two concepts work together for you in your ministry, the more effective leader you will be. Strive for Christ-like humility and servanthood, but know that it's OK to be inwardly proud of what you do. The difference between ministry work and secular work is that when we're proud of an accomplishment, we let others sing about it. We shouldn't flaunt our own talents and successes, but we should quietly feel inward gratification for them, and that can drive us on to even more success. Accolades will take care of themselves.

Now, let me climb a little higher onto my soapbox. As paid ministry staff, do you see yourself as an amateur or a professional? Pause here and answer the question before proceeding. Name three reasons you feel that way, too.

Regardless of your answer, I'm assuming that we're all striving for the best results we can attain with the time, money, and resources we've been granted. But attitude drives those efforts.

So, do you see yourself as an amateur who strives to do cool things the best you can, but you believe it'll never be as good as what someone who works for a major company could accomplish? Or, do you see yourself as a professional who consistently performs high-quality work and always strives to be the best of any group, secular or sacred?

See the difference in attitude? Even though we all want to do the best, it's our attitude about our aptitudes which makes the difference.

To go more in-depth, "amateur" means:

1. a person who engages in a study, sport, or other activity for pleasure rather than for financial benefit or professional reasons.

2. an athlete who has never competed for payment or for a monetary prize.

3. a person inexperienced or unskilled in a particular activity.

4. a person who admires something; devotee; fan. [3]

Hopefully, you're in ministry because you love it and it brings you pleasure, as stated in the first definition. However, you also need to provide a roof over your family's head, food on the table, clothes to wear, etc. So, you also work for financial reasons. However, your financial reasons aren't based on getting rich. The third definition is important for technical ministers. If you see yourself as a professional, you're likely not inexperienced or unskilled. In fact, you were likely hired because you were very experienced and skilled.

---

3   Dictionary.com

In contrast, "professional" means:

1. relating to a job that requires special education, training, or skill.

2. done or given by a person who works in a particular profession.

3. paid to participate in a sport or activity

    •   characterized by or conforming to the technical or ethical standards of a profession

    •   exhibiting a courteous, conscientious, and generally businesslike manner in the workplace.

4. having a particular profession as a permanent career.

5. engaged in by persons receiving financial return. [4]

How many times have you been introduced to someone who does what you do in ministry, except they do the same thing in the secular world? I've heard it phrased as, "Bob does video production too, except he does it professionally." An introduction like that almost makes me want to puke! (That's a technical term!)

If you review each definition of "professional" by itself, you'll see that ministry work is certainly professional work:

1. Technical ministers have special education and training, and they must be able to demonstrate technical skills.

---

4   Dictionary.com

2.   Technical ministers work in the particular profession of technical ministry.

3.   Technical ministers are paid—or at least they should be. Technical ministry isn't a sport, but it's certainly an energy-depleting activity.

4.   Technical ministers constantly strive for high standards. Hopefully, we exhibit a courteous, conscientious, and business-like manner.

5.   Many technical ministers feel their ministry job is part of their calling and hope to do it for a long time.

6.   If technical ministry wasn't a legitimate career, the church would lose highly knowledgeable professionals because they wouldn't be able to financially provide for themselves or their families.

So, at what point are technical ministers not professionals?

And that's my point.

Now, I'll slowly climb off my soapbox.

Part of this problem is others' perception. Many technical ministry jobs are created out of necessity, and in many cases the selection process for employment has been lenient. In the early days of technical ministry, from the late 1980s through the 1990s, being a church member and knowing how to set up a computer and run PowerPoint were the only prerequisites for the job. Audio engineers were a little more scrutinized, but lighting operators who could turn a light on and off were brought on board with open arms.

It's no wonder that many onlookers in the early years of technical ministry may have developed lower opinions of those involved. Unless such technical ministers were employed by an audio, video, or television company outside of their church, few church members would have called them "professional." If they did have such secular credentials, then the church was likely ecstatic to have them—because they were "professionals."

Fortunately, technical ministry has greatly matured. There are those in ministry who are as knowledgeable and talented as anybody, anywhere. Some of the most creative and technically complex technical presentations happen in churches these days. This isn't to make our worship services a production or to flaunt our great technical skills. This isn't to show off all the cool technical toys our churches have in order to one-up the megachurch in the next town over.

We work hard and well to glorify the Father through the greatest distraction-free worship we can produce so that our congregations can worship like they have never before. It takes great production skills to pull off distraction-free worship. If we do our jobs right, the congregation never knows we were there outside of any special presentations we may do here and there. Participatory worship should always be distraction-free. When it isn't, a worshipper is pulled out of the moment and begins focusing on the technical part that wasn't right. Attaining distraction-free worship is evidence of a competent crew—and a very capable and professional leader.

As a technical ministry leader, you are not an amateur. You are a professional. If you don't currently believe that about yourself, start doing so, and you should notice a significant change in the kind of work you expect from yourself and your team.

The only time you won't be a professional as a technical ministry leader is when you choose not to apply yourself to your ministry in order to attain the highest quality work possible, which is what our Lord deserves.

"It could be an expensive repair,
or it could just be the plug is out."

*Image licensed through Stockphotos.com by Marty Hill and Quaddot Productions.
Used by Permission.*

KNOWLEDGE AND HUMILITY

REVIEW QUESTIONS

1. How would you rate you knowledge for your job on a scale of 1 to 10?

2. How your knowledge affect you attitude towards those you lead who do know as much?

3. How well do you accept those who actually know more than you?

4. How much emphasis have you put on humility in your life up to now?

5. How well do you do with other's successes?

6. How well do you own up for mistakes, errors, faults, etc.?

7. Can a minister also be a professional? How?

CHAPTER 2
Working with Pastors & Other Ministry Leaders

I have had the privilege to work with some great pastors (and other ministry leaders) who understood the needs and feelings of their staff, and they managed us according to Christian principles. The joy of working with them continues long after the job relationship is ended, for a life-long bond has been forged, based on the brotherhood of the unity in the Holy Spirit we shared. There are countless great pastors, ministers and other Christians leaders who go over and above to be not only great men of God but great servants in ministry of those serve alongside them.

It is this type of leader to whom this chapter is NOT written about.

I've also worked with some leaders who ran their church or Christian organization with a stern hand or extreme micromanaging, alienating the very staff that assisted them in ministry. In the pulpit, the one's who were pastors preached love, peace, and understanding, but when it came to their staff, those words didn't seem to get applied. They literally failed to practice what they preached!

Those are the opposite ends of a broad spectrum. Christian leaders align all throughout that range. In fact, I believe most find the middle. While some strive toward the upper end of that spectrum, some are harder to work with than others. If you've been in ministry long enough and have worked for at least a few different types of pastors and other leaders, I imagine you could tell me your own success stories—and horror stories.

What surprises me is that the topic of working with these type of ministry leaders, whether they are pastors, directors, supervisors, or in some other ministry function, is that they are often only discussed behind closed doors (or not at all). I understand the reasons: staffers don't talk because they don't want to lose their jobs, or they're anti-confrontational, or they believe it's the "Christian thing" to do. Whatever the reason, open discussions about working for such a leader in ministry seems taboo in most places.

For instance, countless resources exist on how to be a better leader of the church, but where are the books and resources on how to be a better leader of the church's staff? While I'm sure a few exist, I sometimes wonder how many pastors pause to evaluate themselves in regard to leading their staff. Do they seek to discover if they're actually a micro-manager, or if their staff is losing respect for them? Do they look for helpful feedback from the people with whom they serve the church at large?

But this cuts both ways. Few resources exist on how to be a better church staffer or how to understand better the pressures and daily stresses of being a pastor and a boss. In other words, I think those who work in the church, from every pastor to every staffer, all need to work on better understanding each other.

And because you're a church staffer, your job is to learn more about your pastor so that you might be able to serve your church better. This involves knowing how to identify your pastor's managerial style and knowing how to best work within their style. Sometimes, it also means knowing when it's time to move on to a new gig.

In the meantime, while you're at your current job, it's important to realize a few things.

Let's start with what the Word says.

First, we are called to obey those in authority over us:

> *"Obey your leaders and submit to them, for they are keeping watch over your souls, as those who will have to give an account"*
>
> *Hebrews 13:17*

Next, we are called as ministers to preach the Word and to make disciples:

> *"I charge you in the presence of God and of Christ Jesus, who is to judge the living and the dead, and by*

his appearing and his kingdom: preach the word; be ready in season and out of season; reprove, rebuke, and exhort, with complete patience and teaching"

2 Timothy 4:1–2

Finally, we are called to serve:

"Whoever would be great among you must be your servant, and whoever would be first among you must be your slave, even as the Son of Man came not to be served but to serve"

Matthew 20:26–28

Remember: we are technical ministers, meaning we are called to obey, to preach, to make disciples, and to serve. If we're not doing that above all, we're not doing our jobs.

"I will of course yield to whomever agrees with me."

Image licensed through Stockphotos.com by Marty Hill and Quaddot Productions. Used by Permission.

How to Identify Your Pastor's Managerial Style

Although styles fall all along a spectrum, let's keep this simple: pastors can lead confidently or insecurely. The confident pastor relies on God and his staff. He trusts his people to strive toward accomplishing work that advances the Kingdom. The insecure pastor relies on himself, falsely believing that if he's not steering the ship, no one is. He trusts himself to do the work of the church. The confident pastor seeks to use his staff to their fullest potentials. The insecure pastor seeks to use his staff as a crutch: only needed when absolutely necessary.

The confident pastor understands that his staff was hired based on careful hiring procedures, and based on their particular gifts they were placed in positions where they could thrive. He leads them in directing the ministry of the church, but he releases them to perform their duties as they see fit. He trusts that their actions are motived by their best intentions to further the Kingdom.

When a confident pastor relies on his staff, the staff is happy, content, and can't believe they get to serve on such a team. They can't wait to get into the office and interact with their coworkers, volunteers, and church members. Their ministries witness success. And, as it is in the secular world, the more successful the staff, the more successful the leader is seen to be.

However, things turn when, as mentioned by John Gilman of ACS Technologies,

> "Some ministry leaders have such a strong grip on their ministry that no one can do anything without their approval. That's not leading by the Spirit. That's leveraging the flesh. People should serve alongside you in ministry, shoulder to shoulder. They shouldn't serve so far underneath your feet that they are crushed."[5]

Then there is the insecure pastor who micromanages. It's "My way or the highway" at all turns. While the insecure pastor may say he's open to listening to ideas and gathering feedback, his responses and actions reveal his true thoughts. If it's not his way, his design, or his idea, then "It just isn't right." He'll insist on changing a staffer's idea to accommodate his wishes.

Church staffs that work for an insecure leader will often feel frustrated and stymied. Their ministries see little to no growth. The congregation may be oblivious to these issues, but they may still sense that something just isn't right. They're indirectly influenced by the malaise that sets into a staff under the leadership of an insecure pastor.

Because he's the one who's been ordained to lead that flock, such an insecure pastor is convinced that what they're doing

---

5   http://www.acstechnologies.com/blog/ministry-leadership/9-ways-lead-eyes-hands

is God's way. Therefore, everything they want must also be God's will. In such an environment, little room for creativity exists. I know this from experience.

I once worked for an insecure pastor who would tell me, "Show your creativity." But when I constantly failed to show him his version of creativity, he slammed me for not sticking to his plan. Then, when I stuck to his plan—even though I knew it wasn't working—I'd get chastised for not being creative enough. I lived these Catch-22 moments over and over. I couldn't win, and my frustration levels increased on a daily basis. I'd try to do the same thing three or four times in different ways in a vain attempt to discover what he might like or at least accept. But nothing was ever good enough.

Instead of exercising my gifts in technical creativity, I assumed a purely defensive mode in all of my work, and all of my work suffered. The final nail in the coffin of that professional relationship occurred when he told me, "It seems the creative bus has passed you by." (I didn't bother to reply with, "Creative bus? Really? That's the best you can come up with?" I guess I might still be a little upset by his statement. [Sidebar note for your and my pondering: Study more on forgiveness here. When is saying "I forgive" truly forgiving?" This will be a devotional topic for a future marty-hill.com blog perhaps.])

After I was no longer under that pastor's authority, I found freedom to create. The period that followed that frustrating time in my professional life resulted in some of my best work. That's the notable difference that a leadership style can make.

Brave staffers may attempt to communicate their problems to an insecure leader, but their vented frustrations often fall on deaf ears. A few will change their ways, and some will change for a while before returning to their previous, comfortable, insecure leadership style. But I fear that many will not change and in fact become insulted that their leadership style was ever questioned. They may even ask that staffer to move on to greener pastures.

So, if you can't talk directly to a pastor whose leadership style is less than desirable, what can you do?

How to Work with Your Supervisor's Leadership Style

How well you're able to work within your supervisor's leadership style will determine how long you remain at your job, how your role is perceived, and the levels of respect you receive from your boss, your coworkers, and your church. In other words, adapting yourself to his leadership style will help you and your church in more ways than just strengthening your employee/employer relationship.

Honestly, this section would be better titled, *"How to Work with Your Insecure Boss's Leadership Style."* If you happen to work for a confident pastor or other ministry leader and you're on the same page, then congratulations! You can very likely look forward to a long working relationship and probably a good friendship. Confident leaders make it easy and even attractive to work for them because they're on God's mission and not their own.

Ironically, even when a confident pastor insists on his way over his team's, the respect and goodwill he's earned with his staff will signal how important that issue must be to the pastor. When a caring and listening pastor demands his will, it's usually understood by the staff that this is a rare occasion. Because they know the heart of the man behind the decision, it will often be easier for his subordinates to comply with his directive without question. In fact, because such a request is so rare, they'll put in concerted effort to accomplish his goal because they don't want to let him down. Such a greater effort in the Lord's work, done with a happy, humble heart, reaps blessings. Through it all, the church staff knows that they're not working to appease their pastor, but rather to serve God, whom they know their pastor is trying as best he can to follow.

Pastors struggle with the fact they are expected to be if not perfect, close to it. They are to be everyone's role model. They struggle with the issue that their personal problems usually stay private and not openly transparent although some have figured out that there are times this ministers to others if used wisely. They also have to deal with the fact the church members will leave. Most of the time, though, they won't leave the "church," but will go to the other church down the street. Then having to understand the changing technologies, and feeling as if they might have to compete with the evangelists on the television or the mega-church across town, keep appealing to the consumer mentality of the 21st century congregation, then the stresses just keep snowballing. Eventually, it can work into his home life and along with marital issues along with, in extreme cases, sexual infidelity temptations.

When we remember that pastors are humans just like us, with as many stressors as we experience (if not many more), we should be able to empathize better with them, no matter where they are on the leadership spectrum.

That said, it's still difficult to work for an insecure leader. Such pastors may have been trained, conditioned, or brought into the church to be in total control. Consequently, some default to micromanaging. By exerting control over everything they can, they're striving to conceal their insecurities. They may not even be aware that they're doing so. Rather than exposing their weaknesses, they feel like they're showing confidence and leadership through such minute managing. But such control is a facade they feel they must keep up so as not to appear weak or imperfect.

Insecure pastors also feel heavy pressure to produce. Whether that means more baptisms, more people in the pews, more dollars donated, or a bigger building, such pastors feel that they alone have to carry the weight of the church's expectations. They are reluctant to trust those around them in fear that they might be let down by their staff, volunteers, or church members. They push and push to the point of alienating the very people they need to help them achieve the church's mission.

At some point, they run the risk of causing the failure they thought they were working so hard to prevent. Such a leader, who mistakenly believes his weakness is his strength, is a tragic hero—just like Anakin Skywalker. In Episodes I–III, Anakin feared losing the woman he loved, but the actions he took to secure her love eventually caused his downfall. Fortunately, he redeemed himself in Episode VI as (spoiler alert! As if you haven't seen it!) he saved his son from Emperor Palpatine. (This wouldn't be a proper tech book if I hadn't referenced Star Wars at least once.)

If an insecure pastor fails to realize his flaws and forgoes changing himself to right his wrongs, his professional story will be tragic. But if God reveals to him how he's falling short of his calling as a leader, his professional story will be redemptive. I encourage such a pastor to consider this:

> *"If we confess our sins, he is faithful and just to forgive*
> *us our sins and to cleanse us from all righteousness."*
>
> *1 John 1:9*

And if that pastor realizes his leadership shortcomings and comes to you in a spirit of forgiveness, you would do well to recall this scripture:

"Pay attention to yourselves! If your brother sins,
rebuke him, and if he repents, forgive him."

Luke 17:3

Then you may just begin to enjoy what it's like to work for a confident pastor, secure in his standing with God as the leader—or, better put, the steward—of his church.

But if an insecure pastor fails to change, you have one more option.

How to Know When It's Right to Quit

Although God may have been stirring low-level thoughts and feelings of discontentment for a long time, you may feel stuck in your position for a number of reasons. I encourage you to use this time to rectify the situation or at least to seek clarity on what those low-level thoughts and feelings are really trying to tell you.

1. Confide in your spouse.

Early on, tell your spouse that you're wondering if the writing is on the wall about moving on. While you don't want verbalized, negative thoughts to take hold and become reality, your possible decision to leave should still be talked and prayed about. Your spouse may have some comforting thoughts that might bring you patience to endure until God's will in the situation is more clear.

"Count it all joy, my brothers, when you meet trials of various kinds, for you know that the testing of your faith produces steadfastness. And let steadfastness have its full effect, that you may be perfect and complete, lacking in nothing."

James 1:2–4

Your spouse may totally agree with you and offer other viewpoints of which you weren't aware, which may confirm it's time to move on. If you and your spouse agree during this time, this situation is much different. It's when you and your spouse aren't on the same page that feeling stuck at your job becomes even more frustrating.

2. Don't gossip or complain.

Speaking to your coworkers about your frustrations can be risky. Undoubtedly, this will happen in a workplace with unhappy employees, but there are serious pitfalls if you fail to corral your tongue. As Christians, we don't want to fall victim to gossip or becoming that toxic employee.

While you may not be happy in the way your job is going, you're still in ministry. It's important to remember that ultimately you serve the Lord. Everything you do reflects upon Him. Employees can have conversations about their workplace environment, but you must be on guard to sense the difference between professional conversation and destructive gossip.

You must also be cognitive of your attitudes and the impressions you leave on others. While it may be obvious that you're not as happy as you used to be, you should not constantly appear angry or displeased, or reveal any other emotion that brings others down who are serving in ministry. While you're there, you should be building others up, always serving in humility. How can you serve in humility if you're grumbling about how unfair something is? Doesn't that become all about you and none about serving?

3. Speak to your boss.

Air out your feelings, but don't become heated. Vent your frustrations, but don't blame. Speak truth, but always speak it in love. Depending on how long you've been harboring ill will toward your boss, such a conversation may be difficult, but it won't be as difficult as enduring another month or another year of enduring the same kind of daily work environment.

If your boss holds true to his calling and respects you both as a person and a coworker, he may change. On rare occasions, such a change may work. Sometimes we all need someone else to tell us how others perceive us, and this is particularly hard to get in an employer/employee relationship. However, in my experience and the stories I've heard from other church staffers, seeing an insecure leader change from one conversation is as difficult as getting a leopard to change its spots.

4. Speak with the elders.

Of course, "elders" could signify a number of people depending on your church's structure. The point is that you schedule time with those who have responsibility for overseeing church leadership. You'd do this because the church is your church too and you only want the best for it. However, such a move could be perceived as a disgruntled employee trying to go around his boss instead of talking directly to him (See Step 1). Often, this approach backfires and may leave you with no alternative but to look for employment elsewhere.

5. Seek employment elsewhere.

This is the nuclear option when you feel confident there is no chance the situation is changing. You've done most if not all the steps above, maybe even some not mentioned. Having exhausted all of your resources, all of your energy, you find your hope of things improving is nonexistent. You have been the optimist. You have tried to make it work. You may have thought you could adapt, but now have sensed God is closing the door on this chapter.

If you seek this option, and you are married and have children in school, consider how this change will affect them. Talk this through at every step with your spouse and be certain they are on board with it. Pray together about it. Older children rooted in their schools often have a tougher time with moving if it involves leaving their school or friends. This cannot be taken lightly and is a valid issue to be considered. Pray and discern God's will as a family in this. Hopefully, everyone would be united in the decision.

The job search process is beyond the scope of this book. If you want to remain in technical ministry, there are resources available to help. Start with those people and churches with whom you already have relationships. Transitions are quicker and smoother when both parties already are acquainted with each other.

Technical ministry opportunities are often listed through various online sites. ChurchStaffing.com and Churchjobs.com are examples of Christian job boards. Many church websites will also post employment listings.

What If That Insecure Leader Is You?

So far, this chapter has dealt with how to get along with your pastor, but what if your subordinates had read this chapter? Where would they have placed you on the spectrum from insecure to confident leader?

It's often easy to complain about those in authority over you. After all, they can make your working life great or miserable. And it's certainly easier to complain about your leadership than it is to assess your own leadership. When is the last time you stopped to consider how your team and your volunteers may feel about your leadership style? If it's been a while, pause now and try to rate how well you've been leading over the last year. Read back through this chapter and honestly ask yourself which parts may apply to your leading.

If you're leading by example and demonstrating humility and servanthood, you're likely doing a good job. With those two virtues working your life, many of the negative issues listed in this chapter are minimized or even nonexistent.

But we're all human, and none of us is always the best leader we know we could be. The next time you're tempted to act in a negative or relationship-damaging way while leading your team, pause and ask yourself,

> "Am I about to become the type of leader I hope I never have?"

This practice can apply to the rest of your life as well.

> Before pointing fingers, vindicate yourself first.

If you can't do so, then you know what your first course of action must be:

Judge not, that you be not judged. For with the judgment you pronounce you will be judged, and *with the measure you use it will be measured to you. Why do you see the speck that is in your brother's eye, but do not notice the log that is in your own eye? Or how can you say to your brother, **"Let me take the speck out of your eye," when there is the log in your own eye? You hypocrite, first take the log out of your own eye, and then you will see clearly to take the speck out of your brother's eye.***

Matthew 7:1–5 (emphasis added)

How can you fault others when you're first at fault? And don't you hope that other people would treat you with this same kind of respect, vindicating themselves before placing blame elsewhere?

Maybe this chapter could have been just thirteen words long. The best kind of leadership that's confident, personal, and God-glorifying begins by following one of the simplest of Jesus' commands:

"As you wish that others would do to you, do so to them."

Luke 6:31

Confident leadership begins with you.

You cannot control what others do; you can only control you.

Become so contagious with your faith that it can't help but infect others.

As you strive to be more like Christ, evidence of your servanthood will naturally shine through you and into the lives of your friends, your team, your volunteers—and maybe even your boss.

WORKING WITH PASTORS & OTHER MINISTRY LEADERS

REVIEW QUESTIONS

1. How would you characterize your current pastor, ministry leader or supervisor's managerial style?

    - Understands the needs and feelings of the staff and strives to work according Christian principles.

    - Understands the needs and feelings of their staff, but often forgets and pushes too hard for their own objectives.

    - Totally oblivious to needs and feelings, or just doesn't care, and micromanages while running everything with a stern hand.

    - Alienates most, if not everyone on staff, while being unaware of their actions. Justifies all of this by thinking everything is being done according to God's will.

2. Do you feel you could safely approach your pastor or leader with an issue about their leadership style, or would you be more afraid your job would be in jeopardy of you did?

3. How do you see insecurity playing a role in a leader's management style?

4.   What struggles outside of the church have you observed pastors and leaders endure that has affected their ability to lead in ministry?

  • How was it handled?

  • Was it resolved?

    • If so, how?

5.   Have you ever left a ministry position because of the managerial style of a ministry leader to whom you reported? Discuss that.

6.   Before reading this chapter, have you ever stopped to consider that, if you supervise people as well, that you might also be this type of person to those under you?

  • Why are you?

  • Why are you not?

CHAPTER 3

Event-Planning: Working With and Supporting Other Ministries

At the core of our calling, of course, we serve the Lord. After Him, then we serve others. We serve our churches, our pastors, our volunteers, and our staff. Rob, a Technical Director (TD) at a church in Texas, knows how to serve wisely:

> I started working as the new Technical Director at a church that has existed for over fifty years. Before hiring me, they never had a full-time TD. Previously, TDs were volunteers, and none had any experience in the world of technology in a house of worship. They were just good people leaders.
>
> When I first visited the church, the first item that caught my eye was the worship pastor leading worship with a headset. The sound was brittle with no warmth or low-end, and he sang many parts as a bass/baritone. After I started my new job, my first question to him was, "Whose idea was it to have you lead worship with a headset?" His response? "MINE!" I knew already to back off and not press it.

One week passed, and we were in our quality assurance meeting to discuss what went well and what needed to be improved. I asked him, "Why do you prefer using the headset?" He responded, "I like my hands to be free when I am directing the choir and congregation in worship."

A second week passed and in our weekly QA meeting, I made the comment to the worship pastor that I was working hard on the EQ settings for his headset. I was working on removing the brittleness and trying to warm up his vocal. The headset he wore was a high-end headset, but its design and purpose was for speech, not singing.

A third week passed and we were once again in our QA meeting. It is discussed that the coming weekend will be a worship service that will have the worship pastor playing piano and leading the church congregation in song. No choir, no band, no orchestra. "Simple Worship" is what they called it. I asked the worship pastor, "Can I put you on a hand-held mic on a boom stand this weekend for this special service?" He responded, "Sure." We went through rehearsal, and I used the best hand-held wireless mic we had in inventory. His vocal sounded awesome, and I told him. He ignored me, knowing that I was opposed to his wearing the headset mic.

What was unique about the "Simple Worship" service is that the band, orchestra, and choir were all in the congregation singing along with the worship pastor. Normally, they are on stage. Following the service, many of the worship ministry team approached him and expressed how beautiful his voice sounded. They had not heard him sound so good.

I received a text message later that afternoon that he wanted to switch to using a hand-held microphone for all future worship services. I sent a smile emoji back.

As Rob's story demonstrates, it's very important that you strive to offer your best to every ministry you serve and do so while honoring those whom you're serving. How you work with and support other ministries within your church is a direct barometer of how the church body views your ministry. Your service to other ministries also reveals whether your technical ministry is really making a difference in the life of the church.

But how is that possible when multiple ministries may clamor for your finite time, attention, and resources? Or what if you're a one-person technical ministry, or your tech team is only three volunteers deep?

In the discussion that follows, keep these excellent verses in mind:

> "We ask you, brothers, to respect those who labor among you and are over you in the Lord and

admonish you, and to esteem them very highly in love because of their work. Be at peace among yourselves"

1 Thessalonians 5:12–13

"As each has received a gift, use it to serve one another, as good stewards of God's varied grace: whoever speaks, as one who speaks oracles of God; whoever serves, as one who serves by the strength that God supplies—in order that in everything God may be glorified through Jesus Christ. To him belong glory and dominion forever and ever. Amen."

1 Peter 4:10-11

Whatever you do, work heartily, as for the Lord and not for men, knowing that from the Lord you will receive the inheritance as your reward. You are serving the Lord Christ.

Colossians 3:23-24

The Structure of Your Church Affects Your Ability to Support Other Ministries

Depending on your church's ministry and staff structure, your technical ministry role may be markedly different than another technical minister's role just down the street. Remember: doing your work well isn't about copying mega-church trends or trying to accomplish something particular just because it looks cool. You must be able to honestly assess your ministry, your bandwidth, your resources, and your church and then figure out what ministry structure can best support your work in service of the church's other ministries.

Most commonly, the technical ministry directly supports the worship ministry. The tech minister reports to the worship minister. This offers the worship leader full creative control, which is what they often desire so that a cohesive and meaningful worship service may be planned. Such worship services may be planned by the worship pastor in conjunction with the lead pastor, teaching pastor, technical minister, and/or a creative team consisting of church members. In smaller churches, the worship minister and tech director both report to the lead pastor.

Notice that in both structures no other ministries are mentioned. The children's, youth, men, and women's ministries aren't the primary focus of the technical ministry's support. Rather, the technical ministry primarily focuses on the worship service (or special worship events) above all other ministries. If the technical ministry has prepared itself well enough for worship services, then the other ministries may be able to make use of what the technical ministry offers. However, such secondary work would only occur as time and manpower allow. This kind of structure is common in small churches or within technical ministries comprised of just a lone technical director.

In larger churches, a technical director may report to a creative director, a communications director, or an executive pastor. While such a role may still primarily support the worship service, it's usually more expansive, especially if the church has multiple campuses with A/V needs. In my opinion, this structure better advances all ministries since it allows for a larger technical ministry staff, more creativity, and uses resources more efficiently throughout the church while maintaining qualified people in each position. But I also understand that certain requirements must be in place for such a structure to be realistic, like a sizable personnel budget, or dozens of experienced volunteers, or leadership that values what technical ministries accomplish.

Whether you work for a small church by yourself or for a large church as part of a team, you will run into conflicts where you feel pulled by two equally important tasks. So how can you make the right decision and still feel like you're supporting every ministry?

How to Prioritize Your Workload

1. Distinguish regular events from special events.

Regular events are those that happen often, e.g., worship services, Sunday School classes, weekday Bible studies, board meetings, staff meetings, etc. Special events rarely happen, e.g., a yearly women's ministry dinner, a special children's ministry program, special prayer services, concerts, outside programs coming in to use the church, weddings, funerals, etc. These events all come with their own special needs, and there's never a guarantee on the amount of lead-time in preparation for some of these events.

2. Separate regular events from special events.

You know your ministry's weekly needs and deadlines, and you know that you have to meet those for you to keep your job. But does your schedule get scrambled when a ministry comes to you with a special request that they need completed in three days?

3. Write your system.

Having a defined protocol for handling special requests will provide justification for when you must decline such a request or suggest an alternative solution. A written process for handling special ministry-related requests will help you and your team realize when your schedule's too full to help anyone, too. In time, those making the requests should also learn to stop waiting so long to get on your calendar. Though you may experience some blow-back when first implemented, having a defined protocol will ultimately make for a happier team and church staff because they'll likely experience little to no surprises in dealing with a technical ministry with a set plan of action for every request.

4. Create a calendar.

A working event calendar is your best friend. Place all regular and special events that require your ministry's support on it. Even if it's minimal support, the event should be on this calendar with a technical ministry point person's name attached. Any special instructions should be included as well, even if the note is something as plain as, "This class will only use the projector and DVD player." As simple as that sounds, the note signifies that the technical ministry needs check that the projector and DVD player are functional, the remote controls have working batteries, the screen is in place, the audio works, and that the volunteer contact for the class is trained on how to use the equipment so that a technical ministry staff person doesn't have to be present.

5. Schedule three meetings.

This is only a recommendation for supporting other ministries' special events. Through an initial meeting, a setup meeting, and a performance meeting, you should be able to know exactly how you and your team can best support what they are working to achieve.

- **Initial Meeting**:

    Learn about the event and all its details. Discover its scope by asking relevant questions: Who is the event for? Who and how many people will be on stage? What technical resources are needed? Will any videos or graphics need to be displayed? Who's producing those? What stage lighting will be required? What about setting the stage? Will recording or streaming be necessary? If so, who'll be handling any copyright issues? What about IMAG? This is the time to ask any questions that might arise about what could happen.

> ### Special Event Form
>
> Because of the variables involved in special events, I highly recommend using a special events form from the initial meeting to help define the scope of the event. In some cases, you may need different forms for different types of events rather than one form that tries to serve for all events. You must decide what's best for your church's needs. While most forms these days are usually online, the content is similar. A link to samples of special event forms is in the resources section at the end of this book.

- **Setup Meeting:**

  Schedule this several weeks before the event. This meeting is a checkpoint for everyone to report on hiccups along the way or tweaks that may be necessary based on something that might have changed since the initial meeting.

- **Performance Meeting:**

  Schedule this final meeting for the day of the event (or the day before) to ensure everyone that all is good to go. This meeting will also help remind everyone about every detail so that nothing is overlooked. Walk through the program order item-by-item and transition-by-transition to ensure the program flows smoothly. This meeting can be expanded to include the entire production team, or a separate team meeting can be conducted if preferred.

6. Post-Event.

Congratulate and praise your team. Remember: *always give credit where credit is due!*

Then, whether in person or through a form or a debriefing meeting, seek feedback from the "other" ministry point person about the event.

- Did the technical ministry's work meet their expectations?

- What went well?

- What went wrong?

- How could you do better next time?

- Will there be a next time?

- Should we schedule this event for the same time next year?

The Single Most Important Aspect of Supporting Other Ministries

Make sure that they feel important. Assure them that they have a place in your ministry and that you will make their needs a priority. If you do this and complications or scheduling conflicts arise, they will be compassionate and understanding. They should grant you grace when needed and work with you to find a solution.

I've worked in churches and talked with many church leaders where their technical ministries weren't supportive, which resulted in these churches' other ministries becoming very frustrated. After working to resolve their issues, the appreciation shown by the now-very-happy ministries was incredible and heart-warming. A little planning up front coupled with clear communication on all sides goes a long way.

Lastly, consider this.

> *"Now I urge you, brothers—you know that the household of Stephanas were the first converts in Achaia, and that they have devoted themselves to the service of the saints—be subject to such as these, and to every fellow worker and laborer."*
>
> *1 Corinthians 16:15–16*

Servanthood and humility are the keys to ministry, and it's especially true for technical ministries serving the church's other ministries. Let them know you're there to help ensure they succeed, and that you'll do everything within your power to make sure that happens.

Unfortunately, you will fail at this sometimes.

Nobody is perfect, and in the technical world nothing always works exactly how it's supposed to (or at least not for very long). Events do not always go as planned, and neither do planners always convey everything they need to convey. Consequently, you may not have known they needed a projector and a screen in Room 12. But, as far as you can with the information, time, and resources you're given, do as much as you possibly can to ensure their success. Then your work will speak for itself, and hopefully they'll own up to any shortcomings on their end and learn from the experience.

In everything you do, whether for another ministry, the homeless, your community, or your church body, base your work on the virtue which Jesus spoke:

> *"If anyone would be first, he must be*
> *last of all and servant of all."*
>
> *Mark 9:35*

Never forget that your role as a Christian and as a technical minister are one and the same:

Be a humble servant to all.

If you can remember this simple phrase, your work won't be just work; it'll be service from a heart that's glad to worship God by serving His people.

EVENT-PLANNING: WORKING WITH AND SUPPORTING OTHER MINISTRIES REVIEW QUESTIONS

1. Who do we serve?

2. How do you think your church views your ministry?

3. What is your system for defining and planning events outside the scope of the worship services? Do you even have a system?

4. How much emphasis do you put on servanthood in your ministry?

5. Do you feel you serve the other ministries well? Do you feel your team serves the other ministries well?

6. How can you and your team improve in the area of servanthood?

7. Can you ever achieve a level of not ever needing to improve in the area of servanthood? Why or why not?

CHAPTER 4

Work vs. Family Life

Image licensed through Stockphotos.com by Marty Hill and Quaddot Productions.
Used by Permission.

When I began working in full-time ministry, I poured my heart into it because I was starting a technical ministry from scratch. Not only did I want to learn what other churches were already doing, but I had my own ideas of what could be done that I hadn't seen being done yet. I spent far too many hours preparing for each weekend service and studying how we could move into the future of a new area of ministry that was just in its infancy within our church.

I worked so much that I lost track of time. I wouldn't get home until well into the evening. As the ministry grew, my tardiness was sometimes due to creative elements taking longer to create than I thought they would. I yearned for our new ministry to succeed, and I wanted our new creative elements to be top-notch.

Yet I was losing time with my family and alienating my wife. My children were young then and weren't getting as much of a father figure as they needed. I wasn't the husband I needed to be when I was home either. I wasn't open to hearing my wife's pleas because they went against my professional, ministerial, surely-God-ordained goals. Friction between myself and my family increased. I was gaining my whole professional world and yet losing my soul.

The Myth of Work-Life Balance in Ministry

How I wish someone would have written a chapter like the one you're reading and I would have read it when I started in ministry. The sad part is that I probably knew these things deep down, but simply failed to heed their importance. My prayer for you is that you won't make the same mistakes I did when it comes to work-life balance—and especially ministry work-life balance.

Balance is a suspect word when it comes to discussing work and life. Seldom do we achieve balance due to the ebbs and flows of life, family, and work. That's why I like to consider work-life balance as something firmer: commitments. After all, when we discuss balancing ministry and life, we're really discussing the kinds of commitments you've made to yourself, to your family, and to your church. And when it's put that way, it's easy to see why those in ministry may struggle the most with "balance." It's as if we have to constantly ask ourselves, "Who comes first: me, my family, or God?"

This chapter aims to help you think wisely about that answer. This chapter also requires two caveats. As a married man with children, my advice is often geared toward those like me. However, single ministers can certainly apply the ideas in this chapter with regard to their friends and immediate family. (Plus, single ministers may someday have a spouse, and freeing yourself from poor work habits prior to marriage will greatly benefit that future relationship.)

Additionally, though my stories are told from a male perspective, female technical ministers will benefit from my mistakes too. Most all of the issues technical ministers face are possible regardless of sex. The actual stories and perspectives may differ, but its causes are often the same.

Choosing Your Spouse Over Your Job

When starting a new career or position, it's easy to put 110 percent of your effort into it. Problems arise when you put 100 percent of your time into it. Granted, times will come when you must devote more time to your job, but limiting such instances is what's important to maintaining a healthy home life.

I know I would have been a better husband and father had I heeded that suggestion when I first started working in ministry. My problems at home grew exponentially when my lack of time management skills at work became the norm. I rationalized my long working hours. Early on, I never learned to say no to my bosses for fear of disappointing them or even losing my job.

Evidently, the fear of losing my wife and kids wasn't as great. Years passed before I realized what would have been the greater loss.

The Bible is particularly clear about a husband's responsibility to his wife: Paul wrote,

*"Husbands, love your wives, as Christ loved the
church and gave himself up for her"*

Ephesians 5:25

When you consider your work in light of that passage, the question of whether your family or your job is your priority ought to be an easy debate. Work should rarely win over family.

But our careers often win (even in ministry) because it defines who we are in our society. Plus, many of us chose our career paths long before we knew whom we were going to marry. Consequently, career sometimes supplants marriage because we've worked for it for longer. Work is our passion. Work makes us tick.

But then your mate comes along and puts pep in your step and joy in your jump. For a time, it likely seems as if nothing else matters other than that person. You can't help but think about them almost all of the time. Then you promise to hold, love, and cherish them from your wedding day forward. Then you build a house, have children, and share your most intimate self with them.

Then life happens. When the ideals of the married life fall prey to the realities of living in a fallen world, you may fall back on what makes you feel good: work! You get absorbed into your job and maybe begin to (inadvertently) neglect those you love.

More specifically for technical ministers (and shared from experience), we explain away our lateness or absence by saying things like, "It's a special service, honey. It'll be over soon." Only when that one's over, the prep for the next one begins. Before you know it, the work you put in for a special service becomes your new normal. Home takes a permanent backseat to ministry. You deny its effect for a long while and justify yourself under the guise of ministerial responsibilities.

You tell yourself that this season will end, that everything really is OK at home, and that your family will be fine without you for just this one more event.

Then months pass.

Then maybe a year.

And it's only gotten worse because you failed to be proactive in choosing your family over your career.

I pray that if this describes you right now, God will open your eyes.

If not, the results of such work-life imbalance can be catastrophic in a number of ways.

Choosing Your Kids Over Your Job

There are countless movies from Hollywood that show hardworking dads that obviously love their children, but put their jobs first. Meetings go long and they miss a recital. A boss demands a report been done before they leave and they miss a play or a ballgame. This list goes on and on, but includes movies such *Hook* with Robin Williams, *Liar, Liar* with Jim Carrey and *Jingle All the Way* with Arnold Schwarzenegger among others.

One reason Hollywood focuses on this topic so much isn't because they are trying to just do the right thing and help men realize they need to be home with their children. They do it because it is a topic most, if not everyone, can relate to, therefore more tickets are sold, hence a bigger profit margin for themselves. I seriously doubt Hollywood's intentions on this topic are so noble as to be helping society to a more positive position in the family structure.

What is most important is your presence at home.

One thing about a lot of these movies, and one thing I missed with my own children as I started ministry, is that it is more than just making recitals and baseball games, plays and award ceremonies. While those are indeed important, and your child will be searching the crowd for your face, what is most important is your presence at home. I feel I did a decent job a trying to make their events, but I let the job take over from being home like I should have been. That is where everything happens. That is where you teach your children, by your words and by your examples. How do you treat your wife? How you do that is watched by your son and that is how he will be treating his wife.

I have no problem letting my kids see me hugging and kissing my wife. They may laugh and make jokes or funny noises about it, but they'll be reassured of our relationship first, and second, they'll have another example of how to positively treat their spouse. I make sure they know to love and respect their spouse, even when things are not going well. Specifically with my boys, as they got older, we've had very frank discussions about sex and how to treat a woman in the course of an argument. They know violence toward their wife is never an acceptable course of action. They've never seen that from me and they know I will never accept that from them. I fully trust that this characteristic is part of my sons' DNA at this point.

For instance, your children could grow up without as much of your parenting input as they need, which can result in negative ramifications for the rest of their lives. Furthermore, if overworking has you bringing stress and impatience home with you, you're modeling behavior and attitudes that I doubt you'd want your kids to emulate.

Another way to think of this that is actually applicable is an expression from our tech world. We know this as GIGO, or Garbage In, Garbage Out.

Harry Chapin's *Cats in the Cradle* may be the best illustration of choosing your job over your family. While I recommend giving it a listen right now and honing in on the words, many people who already know the song know the story it tells.

A father is constantly too busy to spend time with his son but always making empty promises that he'll spend time with him soon. But soon never arrives. The son grows up, but the father's story never changes—until the very end. Now that the dad has retired, he's home all the time. But now the son has his own career. When the father calls his son and asks him to spend time with him, the father receives the same empty promise he'd given his son for all those years. With great sadness, the father realizes his son is just like him.

Is that the model we want to be for our children? Is that how we would like them to turn out? *The Cat's in the Cradle* proves the adage, "Monkey see, monkey do." You set an example for your children even when you're not there. Your notable absence is the example.

Returning to our movie examples of father figures, *Frequency*, with Jim Caviezel and Dennis Quaid, has another perspective I would like to visit: the absence of the father because he died early in the child's life. Caviezel found he could talk with his dad back in time through a HAM radio via a fluke in the aurora borealis. Together they headed off the things that killed his father, Quaid, until they were both still alive and together in the present. This movie shows the difference a positive, loving father can make in a person's life. Great story line many people would love to have happen in their lives. This movie hits home with me because my own father died when I was five weeks old and my mother never remarried. Growing up, I looked to my friends' fathers for my examples of how a father should be as I had no father figure at home. I had Boy Scout leaders, coaches, teachers, pastors, etc. whom I looked up and watched and studied, but I often feel the hurt of not having a father. That void is real. Even as I write this, I feel it and I still tear up.

However, right now, in this moment,

>WE are alive.
>>WE can be with them.
>>>Now!

Our children are so precious to us. Yet we do not always consider how everything we do affects them.

So be with them.

>At home.
>>At their events.
>>>Everywhere you can!

Be aware of not only your time with them, but also your time away from them. Trust me; they're aware of it.

Choosing Your Health Over Your Job

When I started in full-time ministry, I wasn't in perfect shape, but I wasn't in bad shape either. Although I'd just suffered a weightlifting injury due to a bad disk in my back, I'd been active through playing basketball and volleyball. With ministry, I began a life of sitting behind a computer most of the time. That's all our media ministry was at first: PowerPoint, sermon, lyric and announcement slides as well as publications.

Then, running cables got me moving, but I was still mostly doing static computer work. As I sat, the weight accrued. My time management tanked. My home life became stressful. My health worsened, only I wasn't aware of it because of my weight gain. Everything snowballed.

As the years ticked higher, so did my weight. I made excuses. I'd get upset when it was brought up. I wasn't doing anything different food-wise. I was just getting older, sitting all day, and not eating a healthy diet. All of it was catching up to me.

Finally, in the summer of 2003, I experienced heart palpitations and light dizziness. I'd suffered these issues before, but had never really noticed them. They seemed like they'd always been there.

This got my attention.

I went to the doctor for an EKG. Of course, my body behaved itself for the five seconds they ran the EKG machine. However, the doctor believed my story, so he scheduled an appointment with a cardiologist. After waiting for two weeks, they wired me up for an echo-cardiogram, and the technician started looking at my heart.

She made three passes, put the wand down, and got the doctor. He repeated what she'd just done.

When he finished, he immediately removed my wires, put me in a wheelchair, and took me across the parking lot to the hospital. Within an hour of entering the cardiologist's office, I was in emergency surgery.

A few hours and four stents later, my wife and I were told that I'd had a silent heart attack. I was within minutes of no longer being here.

Thankfully, I've been on medication and have had no real issues since then.

How much of my health issues had been due to my diet or exercise issues or had been job-related stress? Who can say for certain? But stress was surely a factor. After that incredibly close call, I decided that anything which would add stress to my life must be minimized or removed. Consequently, I consciously reduced my job stress.

Overwork and a lack of rest will inevitably take its toll on your health. Eventually, a lack of sleep will lead to chronic cardiovascular problems like hypertension and heart disease. Obesity, high blood pressure, diabetes, and even early death can ultimately result from heightened stress levels. When stress becomes chronic, it will show up in either overeating, under-eating, alcohol or drug abuse, or social withdrawal.

The one simple remedy to this: take more time off.

Yet so few of us actually take time off because we feel that our work is instrumental to the greater work our churches are accomplishing.

But do you know how much work a dead person can accomplish?

The captain obvious answer is - not very much. I've accomplished a lot more since 2003 than I would have had I not survived my rapidly deteriorating heart condition.

7 Ways to Redeem Your Time

If you haven't already identified the areas in which you're struggling to make time (spouse, children, health, etc.), pause here and truly consider where you need to shift your focus to. Read through the following list of seven ways to redeem your time. Pick a few that will serve you best.

1. Every week, carefully plan your time.

Use a calendar. It doesn't matter whether it's on your phone, your wall, your desktop, or in a pocket-sized planner. Since we're technical ministers, I assume most of us use digital calendars, but some may still prefer good, old-school paper planners.

Personally, I use Microsoft Outlook because that's what I've used everywhere I've worked, but it also organizes your information very well. You can create multiple categories and folders for your email and your calendar entries, multiple calendars for different areas of your life, create and receive meeting invitations from others, and set reminders so you don't miss important events, such as soccer games and recitals—much less meetings with your boss. You can set recurring events such as birthdays and anniversaries, too.

I use Outlook for tasks that are new to my routine so that I can get used to them, such as checking the work database each third Wednesday of the month for a specific type of information.

Or, I give myself a personal task reminder that I need to set up an appointment to get my dog's rabies shots.

The list is endless, but it's all about managing your personal, familial, and professional time. For me, Outlook handles it all well. I'm convinced that the better you track it all, the more you'll accomplish and the happier you and your family will be.

2. As you plan, budget in family time.

There may be times you can start your workday earlier in order to be home earlier for your child's afternoon baseball game or piano recital. These are as important as anything on your schedule. While they may not seem important to you, they are the most important things to your child—whether they say so or not.

The point is intentionality. Be constant. Let nothing interfere with your commitment to your family time. If it isn't already, that scheduled family time will become your family's way of life. Your family will become closer to each other and happier. When problems arise, you'll be able to endure them because you've become stronger together.

3. Schedule date nights.

If you're married, plan date nights. Even better, set aside a regular night of the week for just you and your spouse. Get a babysitter for that one evening. Make that night all about your spouse and your marriage—and try not to talk about work!

If you have problems recovering that long-lost spark, then remember how you felt about your spouse before you got married.

- What attracted you to him or her?

- Concentrate on your love for them as pure and as from Christ.

- Let nothing separate your eyes from them on this night. They are your spouse whom you promised to love without condition.

- Give them all your love on this date night.

- Whatever their love language, meet them there.

- Make this night the night you both look forward to above all other nights.

4. Give your full time and attention.

Paul's well-known exhortation to husbands and wives subtly speaks to time management:

> *"Wives, submit to your husbands, as is fitting in the Lord. Husbands, love your wives, and do not be harsh with them. Children, obey your parents in everything, for this pleases the Lord. Fathers, do not provoke your children, lest they become discouraged."*
>
> *Colossians 3:18–21*

One of the keys to doing what Paul says is time. By managing your time, you will be with your family, not just in body, but in heart and soul as well. Taking work home and being physically in the house but mentally miles away isn't quality time. If possible, always leave work at work. When you give your family your physical time, be sure to also include the undivided focus of your heart, soul, and mind too. Your spouse and your children will notice when you don't—and when you do.

5. Get outside help.

If your home life has already deteriorated due to working too much or other factors, seek professional help. If you stay at work as an escape from home, you may have deeper issues to work through. If you and your spouse are having trouble communicating or feel like you're at a relational impasse, consider marriage counseling. That's beyond the scope of this book, but I have one recommendation: if either of you feels that marriage counseling is necessary, don't wait for things to get better before acting on that impulse. Your spouse is too precious, and so many times we lose sight of that in a marriage working against itself.

6. Get inside help.

If your problems at home are more the result of not being able to balance the responsibilities of your ministry job and your family, talk about the challenges with your supervisor. I honestly believe they will be sympathetic to your cause. (They likely will have experienced the same thing themselves.) Most ministers and pastors want their staff to have good home lives. If you fear talking to a supervisor, seek a mentor's guidance. A good mentor will openly listen and then offer good counsel.

7. Read.

When it comes to reading about time management, I recommend Randy Frazee's *Making Room for Life*. He goes in-depth on how to manage your work time and your home time, how to keep them separate, how to keep the Sabbath holy, and much more.

I appreciated this book because it taught me to have a set time to end the day. I learned that it wasn't a bad thing to say, "It's five in the afternoon; therefore, it's time to go home and everything else will just have to wait until tomorrow." As a media director and the only technical person in my church, it was sometimes difficult, if not impossible, to do this. Many reading this will be able to relate.

Admittedly, there were times I let that rule be broken, like the weeks leading up to major services such as Christmas Eve, Easter, or a special baptism service. My word of caution is that many times it becomes easy to convince yourself that every service is a special service!

Self-discipline must be maintained to protect your work-day calendar, and family events need to be given as much weight outside of normal work hours as they deserve. Don't be afraid to say no to things that might infringe upon those events.

I'm amazed by the number of job postings I've seen through the years for church media and technical directors that expect fifty to sixty working hours per week. Last I checked, the norm for most 9–5ers was forty hours. Church leadership should be sensitive to the fact that expecting so many working hours will negatively affect family life, which isn't in tune with biblical principles.

I love the philosophy of my senior supervisor, Gerry True, the Minister of Communication Arts at Oak Hills Church in San Antonio. He supports this family principle and believes that rest is also vitally important. Consequently, we have a team in place who supports a healthy work-life balance in such a way that nobody has to work every weekend. We rotate so that we're always fresh, and the time we have off is valuable family time.

Priorities Shifted

As I continued to work through my own issues, I eventually addressed my schedule and workload by reestablishing my priorities. If I hadn't done so, I'm pretty sure I would have lost my family. Home became—and still is—a huge priority in my life. I learned to leave work at the end of a real business day to be home in time for dinner.

My wife and I have now been married for thirty-four years at the time of this writing. We made it through that rough time, and we've endured some others as well. But our commitment to each other remains strong, and we will work through it all with God's help!

So that I can remember what's important, I like to recall this scripture:

"Therefore be imitators of God, as beloved children.
And walk in love, as Christ loved us."

Ephesians 5:1–2

In many years of trial and error, both in ministry and in my family life, I've learned a simple truth that Jesus revealed through his life and ministry: love is often spelled T-I-M-E.

WORK VS. FAMILY LIFE

REVIEW QUESTIONS

1.   How would you say you are in balancing your work from your home life?

2.   Is work inhibiting you from fulfilling family duties?

3.   Could you be in denial on this topic?

4.   Do you find yourself getting home later more often in the evenings?

5.   Do you find yourself arguing with your spouse more?

6.   Do you justify the thinking that your work schedule provides your paycheck which is more important than relationships because a roof over your family heads, food on the table, etc. are basic necessities that must be provided for and if you do not work more they will not be there? Discuss this.

7.   Have work ever affected your health?

   • How so?

   • How did you handle it?

8.   Rank these things 1-11 (with 1 being most important) in your life then discuss why they are ranked why they are. Should they be ranked differently? How so? What would (will) you do to change that if change needs to be made?

- Job

- Friends

- Extended Family

- Sports I Play

- Sports I Watch

- Social Activities

- Group Bible Studies

- Personal Bible Study

- Spouse

- Children

- God

9. If needed, are you willing to clear things off your schedule in order to have a more relaxed life and to be able to spend more time with your spouse and family?

    - Identify items on your calendar that will enable you to do this and develop an implementation plan.

    - Write this down and post it for accountability and the pray over it with your spouse.

MANAGER

CHAPTER 5

Working with Volunteers: What You Need to Do Before Seeking Volunteers

Now that we've covered the more ministerial aspects of being a technical minister, let's go over the managerial parts. Chief among your responsibilities when it comes to leading others will likely be leading volunteers. Unless you're working at a large church with a large staff, or you're still content to go solo by preference or by necessity, you will need to recruit, train, and rely upon volunteers.

And volunteers—God bless them—can be a handful. But when you have volunteers who could effectively replace you on a Sunday morning without anyone's notice, then your job becomes much less stressful and, dare I say it, enjoyable.

However, because you're dealing with imperfect people (just like you), there will always be the need to bring your ministry into your work with your volunteers. Before you recruit, train, or manage your volunteers, you must fulfil one prerequisite that is all too often minimized, trivialized, or forgotten.

You must pray.

Jesus was right when he said,

> *"The harvest is plentiful but the workers are few.*
> *Ask the Lord of the harvest, therefore, to send out*
> *workers into his harvest field"*
>
> *Matthew 9:37–38, NIV*

When you pray, ask the Lord to send you workers.

There are countless studies on prayer. It is one of the cornerstones of the Christian life. Without prayer, our relationship with the Father cannot grow. As our relationship with grows, so does our faith. Jesus said:

> *For truly, I say to you, if you have faith like a grain*
> *of mustard seed, you will say to this mountain, 'Move*
> *from here to there,' and it will move, and nothing will*
> *be impossible for you."*
>
> *Matthew 17:20*

And with our faith growing, now how should you pray?

1. Pray often.

> *"Rejoice always, pray without ceasing, give thanks in all circumstances; for this is the will of God in Christ Jesus for you"*
>
> *1 Thessalonians 5:16–18*

Pastor John Piper defines "without ceasing" in three ways that are all pertinent, valid, and work together simultaneously:

What does it mean to pray without ceasing?

I think it means three things. First, it means that there is a spirit of dependence that should permeate all we do. This is the very spirit and essence of prayer. So, even when we are not speaking consciously to God, there is a deep, abiding dependence on him that is woven into the heart of faith. In that sense, we "pray" or have the spirit of prayer continuously.

Second - and I think this is what Paul has in mind most immediately - praying without ceasing means praying repeatedly and often. I base this on the use of the word "without ceasing" (adialeiptos) in Romans 1:9, where Paul says, "For God, whom I serve in my spirit in the preaching of the gospel of His Son, is my witness as to how unceasingly I make mention of you." Now we can be sure that Paul did not mention the Romans every minute of his prayers. He prayed about many other things. But he mentioned them over and over and often.

So "without ceasing" doesn't mean that verbally or mentally we have to be speaking prayers every minute of the day. But we should pray over and over and often. Our default mental state should be: "O God . . ."

Third, I think praying without ceasing means not giving up on prayer. Don't ever come to a point in your life where you cease to pray at all. Don't abandon the God of hope and say, "There's no use praying." Go on praying. Don't cease. [6]

2. Pray specifically.

"When you pray, do not heap up empty phrases as the Gentiles do, for they think that they will be heard for their many words"

Matthew 6:7

In other words, don't be vague, defined as "not clearly or explicitly stated or expressed" and "indefinite or indistinct in nature or character, as ideas or feelings ."[7] A vague prayer reveals vague faith.

Another difficulty with vague prayers is that they're difficult to discern if they've been answered.

If you pray,

---

6   John Piper — http://www.desiringgod.org/messages/pray-without-ceasing   Used by permission
7   Dictionary.com

"Lord, bring a lot of volunteers to our tech ministry," what is "a lot"?

Rather, specifically pray,

"Lord, we need ten new volunteers for our tech team."

Ten is a measurable number. When that number is achieved, you'll know that God both heard and answered your prayer.

I once remember hearing,

> "God honors bold prayers because bold prayer honors God."[8]

Bold, specific prayers reveal bold, specific faith.

If you don't believe me, or Mark Batterson who said that quote above, believe the Bible:

> *And they came to Jericho. And as he [Jesus] was leaving Jericho with his disciples and a great crowd, Bartimaeus, a blind beggar, the son of Timaeus, was sitting by the roadside. And when he heard that it was Jesus of Nazareth, he began to cry out and say, "Jesus, Son of David, have mercy on me!" And many rebuked him, telling him to be silent. But he cried out all the more, "Son of David, have mercy on me!" And*

---

8   Mark Batterson —http://www.markbatterson.com/uncategorized/12-prayer-maxims/

Jesus stopped and said, "Call him." And they called the blind man, saying to him, "Take heart. Get up; he is calling you." And throwing off his cloak, he sprang up and came to Jesus. And Jesus said to him, "What do you want me to do for you?" And the blind man said to him, "Rabbi, let me recover my sight." And Jesus said to him, "Go your way; your faith has made you well." And immediately he recovered his sight and followed him on the way.

Mark 10:46–52

The blind man made a specific, faithful request. The Lord honored his plea and made him well. We would do well to always remember this story as we pray.

3. Pray expectantly.

"This is the confidence we have in approaching God: that if we ask anything according to His will, He hears us. And if we know that He hears us—whatever we ask—we know that we have what we asked of Him"

1 John 5:13–15

Having read this, how expectantly do you pray? Do you always believe that he hears you?

Consider:

"But let him ask in faith, with no doubting, for the one who doubts is like a wave of the sea that is driven

and tossed by the wind." Are you a wave of the sea or are your feet planted on the Rock?

James 1:6

Jesus said that when you come to him in faith, "believe that you have received it, and it will be yours"

Mark 11:24

That's expectancy.

Lastly, consider Jesus' words to his disciples, who seemed to doubt so much even when Jesus was right in front of them:

In the morning, as he [Jesus] was returning to the city, he became hungry. And seeing a fig tree by the wayside, he went to it and found nothing on it but only leaves. And he said to it, "May no fruit ever come from you again!" And the fig tree withered at once. When the disciples saw it, they marveled, saying, "How did the fig tree wither at once?" And Jesus answered them, "Truly, I say to you, if you have faith and do not doubt, you will not only do what has been done to the fig tree, but even if you say to this mountain, "Be taken up and thrown into the sea," it will happen. **And whatever you ask in prayer, you will receive, if you have faith"**

Matthew 21:18–22, (emphasis added).

The consistent, specific, and expectant prayers of the faithful can move mountains. So, before using any recruitment tools, techniques, or resources I'm about to provide, promise me you'll do one thing that will make everything else about this chapter better for you: pray often, pray specifically, and pray expectantly.

God has supplied you with gifts and a calling into a position of leadership. Likewise, he has given each of your current and future volunteers the gifts they need to serve in your church's technical ministry. When you ask the Lord specifically and expectantly to bring you these workers, your prayers through the Holy Spirit will honor God and be heard and answered, and God will be glorified, which is what our work is all about!

Four Guiding Principles for Working with Volunteers!

In my years as a technical director, I've found the following principles invaluable with regard to how I treat and interact with volunteers. I highly recommend making these easy-to-follow principles part of the DNA of your ministry. When you approach every facet of managing volunteers through these four principles, your volunteers will want to work and to keep coming back to work.

1. Value your volunteers.

This principle effectively summarizes all of the others, but I place it first because, over time, it becomes easy to undervalue even your best volunteers.

Do you know what "volunteer" means? A volunteer is "a person who voluntarily offers himself or herself for a service or undertaking" or "a person who performs a service willingly and without pay ."[9]

A volunteer may get involved for a number of reasons. Maybe they want to work with gadgets. Maybe they secretly want to run a camera during NFL games and your church's camera operator position seems like a fun alternative. Maybe they were inspired by your pastor's recent sermon on serving the church. Or maybe they want to be involved in producing the worship service but can't sing or play an instrument. Their list of motivations is endless. But the point is this: they serve, but they don't have to serve.

Some may serve for a more personal reason: to feel valued and needed. Then again, isn't that all of us when we do something for others? Remember: when a volunteer doesn't feel valued or necessary, their frustration will begin to mount and a silent, inner countdown begins as to how much longer they'll want to serve.

2. Appreciate your volunteers for what they accomplish and forget about what they don't.

As paid staff, we're expected to get the job done. In most cases, if a staff subordinate or volunteer doesn't finish a task, then the responsibility ultimately falls back to the director. Volunteers not only serve the ministry but you as well. In

---

9   Dictionary.com

many ways, they can make your life easier. Always remember that!

If a volunteer serves for one hour, then honor and appreciate that hour. That's one hour of work someone else (like you!) doesn't have to do. They willingly served the ministry and freed up another person to concentrate on something else that needs to be done.

Value and appreciate your volunteers.

But what do I mean when I say forget what they don't do? Let say that the volunteer who gave an hour of their time only contributed that hour to a two-hour project. It's easy to get frustrated and think something like, "Couldn't they have stayed until the job was done?" Again, they voluntarily gave an hour. That's an hour of work done. Appreciate that. Someone else, another volunteer perhaps, might fill the other hour. Worst-case scenario: you might have to do that last hour yourself, but at least now it's not two hours!

When a volunteer finishes a project with the time they can give to it, make sure they feel valued and appreciated. This underlying theme will be said again and again. Get used to it. Make it a ministry mantra: value and appreciate your volunteers.

3. Remember that volunteers have lives, too.

It's easy to assume that volunteers are available whenever we need them to be, but they have lives outside of church work. How you respond when they inform you that they're not available tells them much about how you value them as fellow Christians. They need to know that they're loved and appreciated. Graciously accepting their conflicting schedules goes a long way toward building rapport, trust, and dedication.

When a volunteer feels bad about declining a role on the team for a service or event, I strive to put their mind at ease. I make sure that they know it's OK, and that I realize they have a life. I've even told them this directly. This builds their esteem, their confidence that they're serving in the right place, and their devotion to both the ministry and its leader. If they decline a requested assignment due to a family event or crisis, let them know that family is a higher priority than button-pushing.

Image licensed through Stockphotos.com by Marty Hill and Quaddot Productions.
Used by Permission.

Strive to ensure that your volunteers know that you know they have lives outside of the tech ministry and that those lives are important and valuable. (There's that word again.)

4. Realize that they're going to make mistakes.

This is crucial. How you handle a volunteer's mistake will often determine how long that volunteer continues to serve in your ministry.

When a volunteer messes up, do you get visually frustrated? Do you belittle or scold? Or do you encourage and train? If you realize that mistakes are inevitable, then when they occur, patience is much easier to find.

Plus, when mistakes are made, refer to the first principle. They don't have to be there! If they also feel as if they're not appreciated or that they're inadequate, they likely won't serve long.

Instead of seeing mistakes as failures, view them as opportunities for training. But, as a leader, you must weigh the training opportunity against the volunteer's experience level. If an experienced lyric operator makes a mistake once, most of the time they'll already know what they did. After the mistake, they will have already thought through the scenario so that it won't happen again. However, if the same operator makes a "new" mistake that no one has done before, then a positive training method will walk them through the error and resolution without discounting them or their skills.

Of course, newer or less experienced volunteers need gentle reminders and targeted training on correct methods. Often, on-the-job training is the best training you can provide, even if it means tolerating a few mistakes now and then.

Now, if someone constantly commits errors during a service, then you must revert to gently stepping in, taking over the position, and demonstrating the correct methods while resolving the issues that may, at that point, be very distracting to the congregation. Again, let me stress the word "gently."

In a stressful moment like that, you must realize that the volunteer may be frustrated, embarrassed, or feeling some other negative or even destructive emotion. By showing love, compassion, gentleness, and understanding in such situations, you will redirect your volunteer's emotions to the more positive.

Sometimes, myself included, we forget to value the person more than the performance. (Did I say value again?) When working with people who are willingly giving of their time and talents to help you and the church, value them for that kind of selfless sacrifice. Allow this esteem to be the foundation upon which all of your volunteer efforts rely upon.

WORKING WITH VOLUNTEERS: WHAT YOU NEED TO DO BEFORE SEEKING VOLUNTEERS

REVIEW QUESTIONS

1. How are we encouraged to pray before recruiting, training, or managing your volunteers?

2. What are the four guiding principles for working with volunteers?

   - _____ your volunteers.

   - _____ your volunteers for what they _____ and _____ about what they _____.

   - _____ that volunteers have _____, too.

   - _____ that they're going to make _____.

3. Complete this sentence then discuss why it is important: Value the _____ more than the _____.

CHAPTER 6

Working with Volunteers: How to Recruit Volunteers

J ust ask! It's that easy. (I wish.) I'm assuming that before recruiting volunteers, you've already prayed (often, specifically, and expectantly) to ask God to send you workers. Now it's your turn to ask the workers. In some (likely rare) instances, you'll receive an immediate yes. Celebrate those easy recruitments. For the most part, you will be rejected many times over before finding the people God already has planned for your volunteer team.

One of the best pieces of advice I've read that I like to apply to recruiting volunteers is from Bill Hybels' Axioms:

> "Never say someone's no for them."[10]

We do this by making excuses for other people before we even ask them to help.

---

10   Bill Hybels, page 78

Why?

Because we assume:

- They're too busy

- They're too important to ask them to do a job like this.

- They do this for their daily job, so they wouldn't want to do it on weekends.

- They're not interested.

- They've never done this kind of work before.

By providing these excuses on their behalf, we're saying no for them without even giving them the chance to use gifts God may have given them and of which we might be unaware.

In addition to making excuses for other people, we also don't ask because we fear rejection. After all, if you don't ask, you can't be told no. But being told no is better than not asking. If you don't ask and later discover that the volunteer could have and would have said yes, then you have to confess to never asking. That's a terrible feeling that will hurt your credibility and self-confidence. Not asking is a failure. Asking and being told no is simply being told no. I know all of this because I was once skilled in the art of not asking and saying somebody else's no.

I was once in a home group with John, a man I knew well and thought exuded humility. John was very knowledgeable and wise while leading our group and giving feedback when others led. He was also the held a high office in our community, a position that was easy to see how well it fit him.

As we grew in friendship with everyone in our home group, I was careful not to exploit my role as a church staff member. I didn't want them to think that I was using the group as my recruiting base. In other words, I was saying no for them.

At one of our routine get-togethers, John and I were talking. At the time, I desperately needed someone to run the camera for the next week because all my regular volunteers were either already scheduled at other positions or unavailable. With this at the back of my mind, John asked, "How are things going at the church?"

Without much thought, I jokingly replied, "Well, do you want to run a camera next Sunday?"

He smiled. "Sure!"

"You're not joking?"

"Not at all. I'd be glad to."

I was shocked!

I'd been saying no for him for so long that I couldn't believe this legitimately humble man would want to serve his church in that way. He showed up that Sunday, we covered what he needed to know, and now the rest is history. He remained part of our volunteer tech team for the duration of my time at that church.

John's service is an example of his attitude of servanthood and humility. It's also a great example of not saying no for someone. A community leader in the seemingly low position of camera operator? I never seriously considered asking someone of his station to lower himself and serve. However, isn't that exactly what the Son of God did? The King of kings wasn't born in a palace, but a stable. He didn't ride in golden chariots but on a donkey. He didn't come to rule in an earthly fashion. He came to save and to serve.

When you encounter persons of high position, don't say no for them. They may surprise you, just as John did me.

Always make the ask.

And if they say no, ask if they know anyone else who could help. If they're notable, influential people, they likely know a lot of people.

Recruiting volunteers can take a lot of different forms, but these are my preferred methods:

1. Have your volunteers recruit other volunteers.

You won't necessarily have to ask your volunteers to actively recruit other volunteers on your behalf, but I've found that your best recruiting tool may be the volunteers already happily serving your church. If they enjoy what they're doing (and feel valued!), they'll tell their friends and acquaintances about their service on the tech team.

At that point, your current volunteer will invite his or her friend to serve alongside them. The friend may say yes simply because they'll already know someone in the ministry and consequently won't be a total stranger. Or, your current volunteer may never invite his or her friend, but the friend may realize how fun it could be to help based on their friend's experience. As in advertising, so too in volunteer recruitment: word-of-mouth works best.

In a similar fashion, don't forget to talk about your ministry wherever you can to whomever you can. Share with others what's happening in your ministry and how it's making a difference. This casual sharing will then prepare people for a big ask later.

2. Invite a volunteer to help face-to-face.

An in-person, face-to-face ask works well because both people in the conversation should be able to tell what the other is trying to communicate. For instance, if you make the ask, but the person hesitates, or makes an excuse, or is suddenly distracted, you'll know that they're trying to give you a "Christian" no. You'll also realize when you need to back off, as many people don't like feeling pressured into doing something (especially something unpaid). You can always talk to that person another time and repeat your ask. But, again, use discretion. Don't talk a prospective volunteer's ear off, and don't constantly ask the same person if they can help.

Take a prospective volunteer to get a morning coffee. Talk to them about serving in general and try to get a feel for their gifts. At some point, without pressure, make the ask. They will likely be honored that you considered them. They will feel friendship because of your effort to meet with them over coffee. Even if they don't say yes that day, you've laid a healthy foundation for the day they might say yes.

3. Announce the volunteer need in the printed bulletin or on your screens' rotating slides.

Church bulletin announcements can occasionally be a good invitation to volunteer, but their effectiveness is limited. Running volunteer announcements is often used because that's how it's always been done, or it's the easiest thing to do. If the announcement is worded appropriately, it can't hurt. But don't expect droves of new volunteers from it. However, there's no limiting the power of the Holy Spirit where praying often, specifically, and expectantly is concerned. If you pray like that about your bulletin announcement, I believe God will honor your prayer.

Rotating slides aren't much more effective than bulletin announcements. My guess is that the people most likely to watch the rotating slides are visitors. They may not respond well to being asked to serve when they feel like they barely know the church. Then again, since new volunteers often come from new members, your slide making the ask might be just the thing that inspired them to not only serve in your ministry but also to join the church!

Also, consider posting the job description. These help possible volunteers know what they're being asked to do before they say yes or no. There are no surprises. Everything is upfront. They're better informed, and there might just be something in the job description that inspires them to say yes.

4. Highlight your needs for volunteers in a membership class or open house.

Being introduced to new members is great in that they can then put a name and face to each ministry. If they have any interest in your ministry, they'll make a mental note and will likely make a beeline toward you after the class is over or will find a way to cross your path later.

When introducing myself to new membership classes, I've been wary to make the ask at that point. The new members are just getting to know what the church believes, how it's structured, who our staff is, and so forth. Making the ask at that point feels desperate, as if we're saying, "Now that we've got you, let's get you serving." I don't feel that this is a great first impression. I wonder how many people go through membership classes only to be pushed away by such asks at its end. They should be made to feel welcome first. Serving can come later.

Even though I've been emphasizing the concepts of making the ask and not saying no for others, I believe there are wrong times and places to do so. Sometimes, that's during a membership class. But, if serving is incorporated into the curriculum for the class, then the ask has almost been made for you. However, above all, the main motivation for the class ought to be exciting the church members about their new church and not pressuring them to serve. You will have other chances to make the ask.

You might also consider hosting an open house event at your church. Twice a year, maybe even between services, and in a high-traffic area, host an open house event, complete with extra staff to help receive prospective volunteers. Provide coffee, snacks, and informational packets that include testimonials, job descriptions, volunteer applications, and your contact information. If you make this event meaningful and are intentional about forming new relationships, you may be surprised at the yeses you'll receive.

5. Post the volunteer need online.

While web pages and forms round out the types of communications that new volunteers can access at their own convenience, they lack a personal touch. While online forms let them take their time in filling out an application, there's no personal interaction. A printed word of encouragement is nowhere near as powerful as the spoken word.

Bulletin announcements, rotating slides, membership class pushes, and web pages and forms will help distribute your need for volunteers to a wider audience—as long as they're paying attention. In my experience, nothing has worked better than face-to-face encounters, where the other person has to pay attention, even if only for a moment.

Regardless of how you recruit, don't use these methods:

- Don't beg:
  "Please volunteer! We need you to help!" While this is technically an ask, it's not a good way to ask.

- Don't threaten:
  "We can't do this without you." Volunteers don't want to feel pressured into giving up their time.

- Don't guilt:
  A friend told me he once saw teenagers walk into the church during announcements wearing handmade signs that read, "We don't have any teachers. Jesus loves me. Do you?" That actually happened. Don't be that church.

- Don't just sit there:
  Not asking is worse than all of the above.

Recruiting doesn't have to be a chore. Experiment with the suggestions I've provided and see what works best for you. If you plan certain times of recruitment into your yearly schedule, then you shouldn't find yourself lacking volunteers when you need them most.

WORKING WITH VOLUNTEERS: HOW TO RECRUIT VOLUNTEERS

REVIEW QUESTIONS

1.   What is the most important step in recruiting volunteers?

2.   What are some excuses you've heard people give for not serving?

3.   What are some ways you can let your church know you need volunteers? Maybe there ways unique to your church that are not mentioned in this chapter. Explore these.

CHAPTER 7

Working with Volunteers: How to Onboard Volunteers

Now that you've received a yes, what's next? Once a volunteer is onboard, you'll need to process the volunteer. There are three different forms and several procedures we will briefly cover here that would help in your onboarding procedure. Those are:

1. Volunteer Application

2. Commitment Form

3. Scheduling Preferences

1. Volunteer Application

A volunteer application gets necessary information: contact information, experience, where they desire to serve, where they are in their faith, and background check information.

An interview enables you to verify their application and discuss their background check. It also gives you a chance to see their heart and discuss where they are in their walk and in their life.

- **Background Check:** The background check is important. You really want to know who you'll be working with. Someone with a history of theft or other criminal activity could be put into a position where they're tempted to repeat their past mistakes.

- **Training:** Once all is cleared, the volunteer needs to be trained. (Note that the order of where training falls in this onboarding process may vary from place to place.) If they have no experience, this is also where you'll have to work to convince them that they can do the job. A well-thought-out training program for each position is best, and it instills confidence in the recruit that they're serving in a quality ministry. Depending on your situation, such training may not be in place yet. This is where your experience and skill come into play. Before their debut service or event, walk them through everything they need to know about the volunteer position.

2. Commitment Form

At a point in your process, do not overlook the Team Commitment Form. This document lays out the expectations for conduct, beliefs, and just the formal act of committing to the team. A time period should be defined, that when completed, the agreement is revisited and resigned if desired. Not only are they committing to serve on the ministry team, but you, as their leader, signs it as a covenant to them, that you will do your best to lead them and help serve.

3. Scheduling Preferences

You'll also need to consider scheduling. How often you schedule your volunteers depends on several factors:

- How often can your volunteers serve?

- How often do your volunteers want to serve?

- How many people are on your team?

- What is your current team rotation schedule?

- What kinds of events are occurring?

- How important is each event?

- How big is each event?

How often a volunteer wants to serve or can serve is a huge factor in scheduling. How well you honor their needs and desires in this area directly affects how they'll feel about you as a leader and the technical ministry. It can also have some influence on their feelings toward the church as a whole. Honoring their preferences and requests makes for happy volunteers.

The size of your team plays a part in scheduling and team rotation because you want to be fair to everyone as much as possible. A large team may mean that everybody only serves once a month. A small team could mean that every person has to serve every other week.

If possible, avoid scheduling the same person on consecutive weeks. You can sometimes get by with two weeks in a row, but unless the volunteer personally requests three consecutive weeks or more, avoid such scheduling at all costs. Otherwise, the cost may be a burned-out volunteer.

Without fail, special services and events will throw off your schedule, especially when you know you need certain people in specific positions because of their competency to fulfill the program's requirements. When possible, plan ahead so that your overall schedule isn't severely disrupted. This helps ensure that you're not hurting the feelings of less experienced volunteers who don't get "called up" for special services.

Take your time on scheduling your team. If done wisely, they'll thank you for it, and when that special event rolls around that requires all hands on deck, you'll thank yourself.

How to Maintain Volunteers

> How long you're able to keep a volunteer on your team is directly related to how much they feel valued, tempered with not overusing them so that they become burned out. You must find that balance.

A volunteer feels valued when they know they've done a good job, are shown appreciation, and feel like they're around friends. It's easy for a volunteer to feel good when everything goes perfectly or when they do a great job of averting a disaster, but what about when they make a mistake or a series of mistakes? This is when your character as a leader is most displayed.

You can:

1. Jump on their case like an angry coach, and instead of pushing them toward further excellence, you unintentionally push them away.

2. Totally ignore them, which pushes them toward uncertainty and decreases their confidence. By ignoring the issue, you're confirming that excellence isn't important—or, worse, that they aren't either.

3. Encourage them, gently explaining what happened and how to work around it. This instills more confidence, assures them that their mistake didn't bring about the end of the world, and trains them for the prevention of possible future occurrences. Remember: mistakes are opportunities for training.

Many creative types are sure of themselves. It's the achievement of excellence that spurs their confidence. The problem is that many have never learned to balance their educated and artistic success with humility. I'm sure you know people who, because of their success, feel like they're God's gift to us all. Either all things have to be done their way, or they're so stuck on themselves that they believe humility is just a subject the pastor speaks on every couple of years.

If this describes you, then I suggest that some soul-searching needs to be done. It's fine to be knowledgeable, have creative success, and lead in ministry. That is a lot of what attracted many of to technical ministry in the first Place. But volunteers are crucial to what we do, and therefore, arrogance and conceitedness have no place in leading them.

Remember what Teddy Roosevelt reportedly said:

> "Nobody cares how much you know until they know how much you care."[11]

Humility and servanthood need to be demonstrated by those in authority before you can expect those under your leadership to grow in humility and servanthood. I've held to these philosophies since I began working in full-time ministry. I think about them daily, and hopefully others around me can see those qualities in me—or at least see me trying to be humble and service-minded.

Some volunteers will be too arrogant to let go of control or too scared to admit that someone else may know more than they do. They feel they have to be the expert. They also might feel

---

11   https://www.brainyquote.com/quotes/quotes/t/theodorero140484.html

that others will lose respect for them by showing weakness. By leading in such fashion, they can easily alienate not only other staff and friends but volunteers as well.

At one of my friend's churches, Joe (name changed) was a new employee hired to lead their technical ministry. Joe had the "expert" chip on his shoulder, and it came to light that he would belittle his volunteers from time to time. My friend was looking to serve in the technical ministry. In time, Joe began showing him how to run the soundboard. Joe asked my friend to demonstrate something specific on the board, but my friend didn't know how to do it. Joe replied, "So, you don't know anything."

Granted, my friend wasn't the most experienced sound tech. But my friend was infuriated to the point that he never wanted to serve with Joe again. He also questioned the leadership of the church as to why they'd even hire someone like Joe. When I heard this story, I was just as shocked by Joe's reply.

His response should have been acceptance of the fact that a new recruit didn't possess all of the knowledge that Joe did. If my friend's position was one that he could have been trained further for, then Joe should have scheduled a training session. If not, then Joe should have had a discussion with my friend about redirecting him to another area within the tech ministry that he might know more about and enjoy better.

But the last thing Joe should have done was the first thing he did. Even if it was a sarcastic remark, Joe destroyed the volunteer—which ultimately hurts Joe's work and the church's mission. He would have done well to heed John M. Knibb's words:

> "Effective volunteer leaders are the 'keys' by which we unlock volunteer hands and minds ."

How to Inspire Volunteers

1. Consider how you can best equip your volunteers on a routine basis.

Give them everything they need to succeed in their respective roles. Offer regular training sessions, brainstorming, etc. Well equipped volunteers are happy volunteers, and happy volunteers are your best recruiting tool.

2. Thank them often.

> Volunteers are priceless.

Tell them that—constantly. Write notes, buy coffee, and give shout-outs wherever you can because they deserve it. That is when volunteers feel appreciated. Appreciated volunteers are happy to help, and happy-to-help volunteers make life wonderful.

Don't view them as unpaid, low-level workers. The worst thing that can happen is for a volunteer to feel that you think of them that way or that they're not valued or necessary. If they do think that and they leave with a sour taste in their mouth, the odds of them returning are slim. As their leader, you may not feel any of this, but if you haven't thanked them or shown any real appreciation, they're likely uncertain as to how much you value their contributions.

Showing your appreciation goes a long way. William Arthur Ward once said,

> "Feeling gratitude and not expressing it is like wrapping a present and not giving it."

Give presents!

3. Practice humility and lead by example.

There will be times when you don't have enough manpower to get a task done in the time allotted. At those times, equipping your volunteers with what they need to succeed is imperative. A leader who stands around and just gives instruction and encouragement could damage their relationship with their volunteers. It's one thing to delegate; it's another to delegate and leave your volunteers alone to face certain failure. Good managers surround themselves with great people who can do the job with minimal supervision.

However, great leaders recognize when they need to give their people the tools to succeed—and sometimes that tool is you. One great leader epitomized this service-minded attitude:

> One day during the American Revolutionary War, George Washington rode up to a group of soldiers trying to raise a beam to a high position. The corporal who was overseeing the work kept shouting words of encouragement, but they couldn't manage to do it. After watching their lack of success, Washington asked the corporal why he didn't join in and help. The corporal replied quickly, "Do you realize that I am the corporal?" Washington very politely replied, "I beg your pardon, Mr. Corporal, I did." Washington dismounted his horse and went to work with the soldiers until the beam was put into place. Wiping the perspiration from his face, he said, "If you should need help again, call on Washington, your commander in chief, and I will come."[12]

---

[12]   Maxwell, John C.. The 5 Levels of Leadership: Proven Steps to Maximize Your Potential (p. 140). Center Street. Kindle Edition.

"Helen, you're the Team Leader,
why don't you jump first?"

Image licensed through Stockphotos.com by Marty Hill and Quaddot Productions.
Used by Permission.

WORKING WITH VOLUNTEERS: HOW TO ONBOARD VOLUNTEERS

REVIEW QUESTIONS

1. What steps can or should be taken to onboard new volunteers?

2. Complete this sentence: How long you keep a volunteer is directly related to much they feel _____. Discuss this.

3. When does your position as a ministry leader allow you an attitude to angrily berate and belittle a volunteer?

    - How is this constructive or destructive?

    - Does this hurt or help the ministry?

        - The volunteer?

        - You as a leader?

4. The two virtues promoted throughout this book are _____ and _____. Discuss why these are so important and how they play a part in our lives as we serve in ministry.

CHAPTER 8

Working with Volunteers
How to Delegate Responsibilities
& Handling Exits

Now, a fine line exists between jumping in to help and micromanagement. When you do jump in to help, do just that. Let the volunteer leader lead and then follow their lead. As long as they're within the guidelines that were laid out when the job was delegated to them, allow them to lead. Let them have the authority to decide, direct, and serve through their own leadership. You will esteem the volunteer and gain their respect.

For Good Friday services at one of my former churches, I allowed a volunteer leader to lead the services. Our main creative challenge involved "live paintings" where we re-created famous classical paintings by placing actors and props behind a scrim. The scrim hid our scene changes and enhanced the visuals of the live paintings. (If you haven't used scrims before, add that to your list of creative ideas to try.)

These live paintings were complex and required weeks of planning. My principle role was finding a volunteer leader to take charge of this specific creative effect. All I had to do was equip that leader and ensure she knew the flow of the service and the paintings we wanted to use. I approved purchases, helped paint, and cut wood. All the while, I followed the volunteer's lead.

We ran into a significant problem when re-creating DaVinci's painting, The Last Supper, and we knew we had to get it right because it's such a famous painting. As most stages do, our stage was higher than the congregation. Placing a flat table on our stage meant the congregation wouldn't be able to see its top. The volunteer leader suggested we raise the back legs to provide a better angle for the audience. But then nothing would stay on the table! So we hot-glued our props to the tabletop, which actually helped solve a set-up issue. We wouldn't have to set the table for every performance. But with the raised table, our actors at the back of the table were partially covered. So we set the back legs back to their original height and cut the front legs down. All problems solved.

The visuals of these live paintings were breathtaking and moving. At every service, that creative element was a home run. Why? Because we had a committed, dedicated volunteer gladly working in her strengths under deliberate, hands-off leadership. If you provide what your volunteers need, they will succeed, and by extension, so will you.

But what if you delegate a responsibility to a volunteer and it comes back surprisingly different than what you'd imagined? Ask yourself, "Does it work, and is it just different than what I would do?" If the answer is yes to both questions, go with it. It's a preferential difference, so choose to honor the volunteer's time, creativity, and efforts and use it. If the answer is no, then you have a teaching moment.

For example, in our pre-HD days, one of my graphics volunteers was inspired to be creative on a particular slide rather than follow our style guide. She used a serif font, where we had specified a non-serif font, and one that was twenty points smaller than what our style guide defined. It looked beautiful on her screen and would have looked great on our worship center screens—so long as you were in the first few rows. But if you were sitting in the back row, 115 feet from the screens, you likely couldn't read the small, serif text, and especially if you were older or had poor eyesight.

She learned three specific lessons that day:

1. What looks good on the computer does not always translate to the screen. Always check your work on the screen from the perspective of the room's farthest seat.

2. Use sans serif fonts almost always. We only use serif fonts on large titles over a background that provides good contrast.

3. Font size is integral to readability. After much trial and error, we had defined certain fonts that were acceptable for general use and their optimum sizes. We had also defined an acceptable range of font sizes.

Her overall lesson was that readability trumps creative design. In a loving, teaching way, I conveyed that if a person on the back row can't read a slide, they'll likely become frustrated, distracted, or both. Distractions caused by the technical ministry are never good because they remove the congregation from an environment of worship and introspection. They could miss what they'd come to church to hear. That's why it's crucial to have a teaching moment with your volunteers, even over something as seemingly inconsequential as font sizes. It's not inconsequential!

Never belittle a volunteer or make them feel inferior. Reaffirm them with the good things they've done while teaching on the logic of the areas in which they've made a mistake. If possible, you might even help justify why they did what they did. Maybe they didn't know the guidelines or understand the reasoning behind those guidelines (which means you might need to write clearer guidelines). It's possible your training wasn't thorough enough to make them aware of those guidelines. It's also possible that they knew and just forgot, or that they simply wanted to assert their own control or creativity.

Above all, they must know that it's OK to make mistakes. Everyone makes them at some point. The key is to learn from our mistakes in order to stop repeating them. In time, they'll become better at their jobs, just like you'll become better at delegating, inspiring, and maintaining a passionate group of volunteer tech leaders.

How to Handle Exiting Volunteers

Your team won't always stay the same. You can't prevent volunteers from leaving, but you can work to handle these situations well.

When a volunteer leaves, it's almost always a disappointment. Many times when you lose one, you're losing someone whom you've invested time in, or you're losing an expert who was an invaluable part of the team. Hopefully, you may also lose someone who became a friend. I say hopefully because not only do our volunteers become people we lead in ministry, but the experiences we share tend to build friendships as well.

Practically, volunteers leave due to moving away, transitioning to another ministry, weariness, or feeling overextended in other areas of their lives. Emotionally, they leave out of unhappiness with their role in the ministry, marital or family issues, conflict with another volunteer or church leader, conflict with you, or they're involved in church discipline, which means they likely wouldn't be allowed to serve until the issue has been resolved.

In the first twenty years of ministry, I only lost two volunteers due to extreme negatives. One man was experiencing marital conflict that led to church discipline, which he didn't accept. He became angry with me when I told him he could no longer serve due to his standing with the church, a decision arrived at by the church elders which I had to enforce. The other instance happened due to church discipline as well, but I fanned the flames of anger by missing this man's wedding due to a health issue, a slight I'm not sure he ever forgave me for as I never saw him again after his last Sunday of volunteering.

When negative circumstances like those arise, you must be open, share what you have to say in love and humility, and then leave the rest to God. I do want to treat others how I would want to be treated. I've now made it a very conscious practice always to look at myself first and ask, "Am I wrong? If so, how do I correct this?"

You can't control what others think or feel, but you can control how you react and display your integrity. You will make mistakes in this area, but you should always have humility and integrity at the forefront of your mind. They should be a vital part of how people see you. For that to truly happen, these traits must become part of who you are.

- Are you humble?

- Are you a servant?

Having these virtues, as well as wisdom, patience, kindness, goodness, and all the other fruits of the spirit, as part of what others see in you will help define you as a ministry leader who seeks to serve others at all times.

Most of us could not do what we do without volunteers. The larger the church, the more volunteers it takes to make things happen. As you lead and grow your ministry, strive always to have the highest regard for your volunteers. Treat them well.

Remember that volunteers want to feel needed. They want to feel appreciated. They want to feel valued.

A pastor can show appreciation from the stage, giving a moment of glory for these special people, but it starts with you, their ministry leader, the heart and soul of the team. As a head coach sets the personality of his team, the ministry leader does the same.

Eleanor Roosevelt said,

> "To handle yourself, use your head;
> to handle others, use your heart."

A leader who loves his job and loves his volunteers is likely to have volunteers who love serving that leader and their church. More importantly, a leader who loves his Lord and who prays often, specifically, and expectantly will have volunteers who also love serving their Lord!

Now that you know how you are going to handle your volunteers in most situations, we can go back to the very beginning of this entire discussion of back at the beginning of Chapter 6 and recruiting volunteers… make that ask!

WORKING WITH VOLUNTEERS:
HOW TO DELEGATE RESPONSIBILITIES
& HANDLING EXITS

REVIEW QUESTIONS

1.   How well do you delegate? Do you:

   - Assign a leave alone?

   - Assign and equip?

   - Assign and micromanage?

   - Never assign. Just do it all yourself. Its just faster that way.

2.   Do you allow volunteers to be creative event though what they do is different than what you would do?

3.   Do you have any positions that only one person can do?

   - How deep is your team in terms of backups?

   - If someone quits, is your team in trouble?

CHAPTER 9

Job Descriptions

O ne singer is a soloist. One vocalist and one guitarist are a duo. But one singer, one guitarist, one drummer, and one bassist? That's a band. Even though each person possesses a unique talent, they're all responsible for making the band sound the best it can be. Keep this illustration in mind as you read:

> *Now there are varieties of gifts, but the same Spirit; and there are varieties of service, but the same Lord; and there are varieties of activities, but it is the same God who empowers them all in everyone. To each is given the manifestation of the Spirit for the common good. For to one is given through the Spirit the utterance of wisdom, and to another the utterance of knowledge according to the same Spirit, to another faith by the same Spirit, to another gifts of healing by the one Spirit, to another the working of miracles, to another prophecy, to another the ability to distinguish between spirits, to another various kinds of tongues, to another the interpretation of tongues. All these are empowered by one and the same Spirit, who apportions to each one individually as he wills.*

> *1 Corinthians 12:4-11*

Your calling may not be preaching, music, hosting, or significantly freezing or sweating as part of the parking lot team, but your role is just as important and integral to the church. You are called to tech ministry.

You belong to the greater whole of those called to work in the church, but a calling to tech ministry is also part of a greater whole. Just like a guitarist makes a band better because of his or her particular skills on that instrument, so too do you bring unique technical skills to your technical ministry team.

We are all technically minded, but we cannot all accomplish the same feats. We are not all gifted in the same way. Some are called to be audio gurus, others to be video virtuosos. Some technical ministers can do wondrous things with lighting. We get to serve in a fascinating (and seemingly ever-changing) area. We ought to cherish our similarities and celebrate each other's unique skills. Together, that's how we make music—behind the scenes.

But how can you ensure you find the right people with the right skills, gifts, mindset, and calling to build a healthy and ministerially minded technical team?

Why You Need to Provide Full Technical Ministry Job Descriptions

You must have clear and concise knowledge of what each job is: its role, its qualifications, its training process, and how it fits into both your overall vision for the tech team and the church's overall vision for its congregation. Seeking volunteers without this necessary information isn't a good idea and can lead to frustrating potential volunteers, if not at first, later as they try to figure out where they might fit in the technical ministry.

In emergency situations when you feel short-handed, lacking job descriptions may not matter, but that will only last for a short while. For volunteers to buy-in long-term to what you're trying to accomplish, you must provide a defined structure for their roles.

Well-defined job descriptions will:

1. Clarify your expectations for volunteer roles.

2. Demonstrate how volunteer roles fit into the church's overall ministry, clearly showing how their job will make a difference.

3. Help you recruit new volunteers by letting them see all the available positions.

4. Ensure that the right person lands in the right position, which often increases the length of a volunteer's commitment.

5. Remove ambiguity from what the volunteer is being asked to do so that they're confident in their role.

6. Promote communication.

7. Provide a basis for performance-issue discussions.

8.   Demonstrate real-life examples of how your church is serving Christ.

Setting clearly defined expectations prior to engaging potential volunteers ought to set up you and your future team for success.

How Not to Write a Technical Ministry Job Description

It is not my intention to insult anyone but I have I've seen many ministries with single-line job descriptions, such as the following:

> CAMERA OPERATOR: Shoot video of the worship services for broadcast, throughout our campus, and for recordings.

> AUDIO OPERATOR: Setup the mics for the worship team and choir, and run the audio board for rehearsals and our worship services.

While these are better than nothing, they pretty much just state the obvious. Do such a descriptions really answer any questions for the volunteer? I guess if the camera volunteer didn't know their church broadcasted anything it'd answer that. But if I were a person looking to serve, would those statements really get me excited for those jobs? Would they excite me about the leadership? Would I think they were trying to do everything top-notch? Or would I think the leadership is doing just enough to get by? I might even ponder that they just are not experienced or knowledgeable in the area.

If it were a small church with minimal staff, and a tech team comprised of all part-timers or volunteers, I'd cut them some slack. They very possibly do not have the time to sit down and create the kinds of supporting resources that we're discussing here. I'd grant them a mulligan—then jump right in and see where I could serve. In other words, I fully understand that some churches and ministries are limited by factors outside of their control (size, time, budget).

But if a church with a full-time, multiple-person staff, a large budget, and great equipment put out such a one-line job description, I'd seriously question their intent and motivation. Do they really want a ministry partner or just a warm body? If you are this size church, and this describes your use of job descriptions, I would encourage you and your staff to revisit this area and give it a makeover

So let's look at what job descriptions for technical ministry roles should include.

How to Write a Technical Ministry Job Description

Instead of just stating the obvious—"We need someone who knows how to work a camera."—try writing every tech team job description by answering these eight questions:

1.   What is the job's title?

2.   What is the goal of the position? (How does the role specifically relate to the church's vision?)

3.   Whom does this position answer to?

4.   What are the job's description and responsibilities?

5.   How much time will be required every week?

6.   How much experience will be necessary, or how much training will be required?

7.   What must-have qualifications are necessary?

8.   What are the benefits to assuming the role?

A Note About Job Titles

Carefully consider the names of each position within your technical ministry. How do you use the terms "director," "engineer," "operator," "manager," and so forth? Make sure you use them consistently.

Also, how those terms are used in the secular world isn't the same way they're used in the church world. For example, TV producers today could be writers, directors, show-runners, or all three (or more). A church producer is often someone who oversees the service. This title's multiple usages gets confusing when you meet someone at a social gathering and they ask what you do. If you say you're a producer and the person you're talking to is a musician, they'll immediately start thinking you can help them get their next music project recorded, or that you must be working on the next big Hollywood movie.

You must also consider how you define paid staff and volunteer staff. What those titles imply can sometimes affect feelings, especially if a volunteer has a "higher" title than a paid staffer, e.g., Lead Producer vs. Production Assistant. I don't think this actually happens that much, but you should still be aware of it. The money issue can be an ugly side of ministry once it enters into the equation.

So, choose your titles strategically. Think them through. Don't just choose them just because that's what the job seems to be (or because you read it in the examples about to follow). Ask yourself, "Are the job titles I'm considering in line with the other titles we use?" If not, work to align the titles.

Examples of Full Technical Ministry Job Descriptions

Certainly, the specific types of tech positions will vary from ministry to ministry. Job titles will vary as well even though they may describe the same essential position. The following examples aren't meant to be all-encompassing because so many variables exist across all of our technical ministries. However, I chose these examples on the assumption that most technical ministries employ these types of tech staffers and volunteers.

You're free to use these examples, but I highly recommend using focused time to make these examples uniquely relevant to your church and your people. In the first example, I've placed the guiding questions above each answer to show you how such full descriptions work, but this isn't necessary, as the remaining descriptions show. The point is that you want your descriptions to answer each of those eight questions.

PRODUCER: FULL-TIME (PAID)

What is the job's title?

Producer

What is the goal of the position?

Ensure that the vision for all services is maintained.

Whom does this position answer to?

While the Producer ultimately answers to the Pastor, Executive Pastor, and any other authority over their defined position, their role with the worship service does have authority to make crucial decisions. However, wisdom would dictate seeking the counsel of those in higher authority in certain extreme situations.

What are the job's description and responsibilities?

The Producer oversees personnel, rehearsals, and overall execution of the worship services, works with the Worship Leader, Technical Director, and other worship service personnel, always striving to unite several teams into one.

How much time will be required every week?

The Producer must attend at least one weekly planning meeting, the one-hour all-team walk-through at the beginning of every weekend worship schedule, the weekly one-hour run-through rehearsal, and all weekend services. Outside of meetings, scheduling team members, recruiting, and media and other service element preparations, such as stage lighting, props, audio considerations, etc., need to be attended to in order to be certain the service is ready for the weekend. Since this is a full-time salaried position, the total estimated time per week is forty hours.

How much experience will be necessary, or how much training will be required?

Previous church production experience is preferred. Technical production experience of some kind is required.

What must-have qualifications are necessary?

The Producer must have a strong relationship with Christ, 2–5+ years in technical ministry, and good people skills.

What are the benefits to assuming the role?

Health insurance and retirement benefits are included. You also get to serve the Lord with great people!

VIDEO DIRECTOR: VOLUNTEER

The Video Director ensures that the vision for every service is captured through the lens. This position answers to the producer.

The Video Director directs the video presentation that is viewed via IMAG, broadcast, and on recordings by defining camera-framing and shot selection, as well as video cueing and graphics. They also enter sermons slides and song lyrics into predefined templates according to scripts provided by the Speaking Pastor and Worship Leader.

The Video Director must be available for the pre-rehearsal studying of the worship order, the one-hour weekly walk-through meeting, and all rehearsals and worship services. They will also prepare all graphics and videos into the systems for the weekends and maintain the systems. As this is a full-time position, the total estimated time per week is forty hours.

At the start, a new Video Director will shadow technical team members to learn and understand current worship services and personnel, learn the switcher's capabilities and limitations, and conduct trial run videography during rehearsals.

Previous camera and/or switcher experience, RTV school, other related experience, or demonstrated aptitude is necessary. Knowledge of proper text formatting in graphic design and experience with ProPresenter is preferred.

The Video Director must have a strong relationship with Christ and good people skills.

This role's benefits include the opportunity to lead in a really cool technical role and serving the Lord with great people!

AUDIO DIRECTOR (A1): FULL-TIME, PAID

Goal: Ensure the vision for each service is supported through the use of quality audio.

Answers to: Producer

Description and Responsibilities: The Audio Director works with the worship team to ensure that all sources of audio are properly addressed, configured, and set up in the system. The A1 also works to maintain exceptional, quality sound in the room at the appropriate sound levels for the event, as well as overseeing other members of the audio team.

Time required: A full-time week, including planning meetings, equipment programming and maintenance, team training, occasional weekend service responsibilities, etc.

Training required: Weekend shadowing and system training to learn current systems.

Qualifications: Previous audio experience with digital boards, Dante, Aviom, SMAART.

> Benefits: Health and retirement benefits, plus continued technical education by staying on top of current technologies, and you get to serve the Lord with great people!

Further examples of technical ministry job descriptions are included in the next-to-last chapter, "Resources" and online. That link is also on the resources page.

Providing such full job descriptions will help you recruit—and keep recruiting—the right kinds of people to positions well-suited for them. Besides letting volunteers know what your open jobs are in advance, they'll also see your organizational excellence, spurring their confidence in you and your team, causing them to want to join such an essential ministry.

JOB DESCRIPTIONS

REVIEW QUESTIONS

1. What are four main things we need to know about a ministry job before we begin filling with staff or volunteers?

2. What are some things that well-defined job descriptions could do for you?

3. How do you use the terms Director, Engineer, Operator, Producer?

    - What other titles might you use or be using?

    - Are you consistent in their usage, meaning, rank, etc. or are they just used haphazardly?

4. How would you rate where your ministry is on having written out, well defined job descriptions?

    - How do you think this affects your ministry?

    - How do you think the opposite condition would affect your ministry?

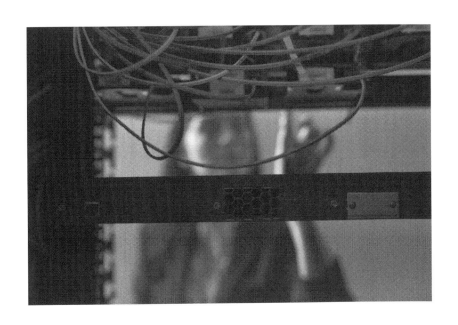

MASTER OF TECHNOLOGY

CHAPTER 10

Video Storytelling

In 2001, we produced and showed a video at Pantego Bible Church in Fort Worth of the testimony of Roger Wells. Just two months earlier, Roger had accepted Christ, and his story was once that only shared his salvation and changed life, but also shared a success story of the church's vision of Biblical community in the neighborhood. Members of the church that also lived in Roger's neighborhood befriended Roger and were able to be God's servants in helping Roger find and accept Christ.

Always looking for stories to tell and inspire our congregation, we told Roger's story in video on Easter morning. Roger talks about how the video affected him and his view on the use of video storytelling in worship services:

> I was very proud after the video of how I came to Christ was shown. I was the guy who had to make everything happen. Always up front because I ran the sales organization, this time I am standing up before everybody for the right thing.
>
> I remembered before this and wondered what are others doing up there, but now this video is

being played and it is my story. This changed how I viewed them. It wasn't that way anymore more and I am just proud of them for telling their story.

Mine wasn't as big a story as some. I wasn't sick with illness, abuse and things like that. I was just a guy who thought, "I'm a good person. I'm going to be OK." But my friends around me knew they needed to get this guy to take the next step. And that was my story.

Many people who approached me afterward were my close friends. Some of the men I played golf at the country club came up and said "I saw you on screen. That was cool!"

You can hit so many more people with video. The pastor is supposed to say those things. It's when someone that isn't a pastor can change somebody's heart. And all these people are seeing it. There might be forty, fifty people or more that identify with that person! "Oh that's my friend!" Look what just happened. I think videos have a major impact on lives because they can see themselves in the story.

It is all so encouraging. I'm just proud of those who share their story. This is not a big stage that is just for me. You have to reach out to everybody you can and when that happens it's very, very cool what God can do.

The Necessity of Visual Storytelling

I may not need to convince you of the value of visual storytelling in your church, but I'm willing to bet you may need to convince other people in your church or on your staff about its value, just as Roger Wells above once wondered why people would tell their story. Because telling well-crafted stories costs time and money, you'll need to be able to argue why creating these stories is worthwhile.

For instance, one of your lead pastors may ask you, "Why do we need stories when we have the Bible?"

Roger hit it on the head with people identifying with the person whose story is being told. But lets look further.

Looking at the Bible we discover that it's more than just a book laying out God's plan for our lives. It's also more than just a historical record. It fulfills these descriptions and much more—through stories. From Adam and Eve through the end of Revelation, pictures are painted as thoughts and motives are revealed. Even when our children are little, we begin teaching with stories, reading them book after book, with vivid pictures that illustrate what we are reading to help them learn the animals, or the alphabet, or morals in a story. And many are the times when we read a small child a story and they say "read it again!" Stories stir the imagination. Stories teach us of life experiences of others so that we can learn from those, whether we realize we are or not. That is because people remember stories. In his The Collected Works, Rudyard Kipling says,

> "If history were taught in the form of stories, they would never be forgotten."[13]

This storytelling method is especially obvious in Jesus' teachings through parables. To help people understand his higher thoughts, he made himself understood through stories. Like Jesus, pastors use stories in the illustrations they tell. And why not? Jesus set the standard for our lives and how to teach.

A church staffer may ask you, "Aren't we already overwhelmed with video everywhere else we look? Why do we have to have them at church?"

Because visual storytelling is a powerful tool to quickly reach the masses. As of December 2016, Netflix has "over 86 million members in over 190 countries enjoying more than 125 million hours of TV shows and movies per day,"[14] and "YouTube has over a billion users — almost one-third of all people on the Internet — and every day people watch

---

13   https://www.brainyquote.com/quotes/quotes/r/rudyardkip134708.html
14   https://media.netflix.com/en/about-netflix

hundreds of millions of hours on YouTube and generate billions of views." [15]

Yes, our society is overwhelmed with visuals, sound effects, music, and more. Multi-sensory overload is the unfortunate norm. But it's also the predominant language of American culture. One of the fastest ways to strike up a conversation with a stranger is to find a point of connection through movies, TV, or sports. Because most all of us consume some aspect of popular culture through the screens we see and access on a constant basis, these are our touch-points. This is our language.

So why shouldn't the church try to speak the culture's language?

This opens the door for some in the church to go down the old road of the usages of technology in the church in general, or even contemporary music. They would prefer hymnbooks, organs and pianos; such as it was when our parents and grandparents were growing up. Let's don't even mention drums and guitars! "The church should never change," would be their mantra.

In regards to visual storytelling, they may also argue, after the expense and manpower, is that it takes up too much time in the service. It takes time to build the story. You have to introduce the character or characters, develop the storyline, establish the conflict if there is one, and resolve it, assuming

---

15   https://www.youtube.com/yt/press/statistics.html

there is a resolution. All of this takes time to do effectively and will usually take away from another element in the worship service.

However, I always like to point out that the church changed when it moved from Latin Gregorian chants and pipe organs to organ, piano and English hymns. Music has changed through the centuries. Therefore, all aspects of ministry are subject to change as well, including the adding of new technologies such as video storytelling,.

Now that we've asserted why visual storytelling should be a language the church learns how to speak, let's delve into the practical aspects of telling compelling stories through motion pictures.

The Ten Steps of Visual Storytelling

For me, the following ten steps represent the most essential needs for any story told visually for church. The first three are questions that you must answer before doing anything else. It's the hard work of sitting in front of your computer and thinking through what's necessary before ever hitting record. The last seven steps are the practical steps you'll need to take to create a great video.

I'm confident that if you follow these ten steps, you'll be able to create quality videos on any budget that can ultimately change lives. Do not ever forget that this is the bottom line of why the video story is being told.

If you are moved in the editing room by the story you are working on, you can be assured that the congregation is likely going to be moved as well. If you are not moved while working on the timeline, and putting the story together, then back away for a bit, review the meaning and depth of the story, and do a reboot of yourself. If you still don't feel the emotional connection to your story, then ask yourself if it's working. I feel the spiritual and emotional aspects of a video should work with you, the editor before they'll ever work with anyone else.

First, you'll need to ask yourself these three basic questions before shooting one frame of video. These in many cases will any dictate some of the creativity questions you may have later:

1.   **Who is your audience?**

2.   **What is the purpose of the video?**

3.   **How long should the finished video be?**

For the most part, your audience will be your church. However, there may be some instances where your video can be used in multiple ways, such as an outreach commercial or on social media. List every possible audience your video might be targeted to.

The purpose of the video is why are you making it and what do you want your audience to do, feel, or think after watching the video? What is the call-to-action. Do you want them to consider Christ's forgiveness, give to the building fund, or invite a neighbor to church? The more specific your call-to-action, the more likely your audience will respond. Remember too: your call-to-action will vary based on your targeted audience. For instance, you wouldn't produce a commercial encouraging possible visitors to contribute to your building fund. (You likely wouldn't want that even mentioned in passing!)

If you've ever watched a YouTube or Facebook video, you know the answer to the last question. We tend to watch short videos these days, and with as much as can be planned in just a one-hour worship service, the time remaining for any visual stories usually isn't immense. Think in minutes, with two minutes or less as a sweet spot. Unfortunately, most of the time getting those two minutes on film could take a hundred times as long to create, which is why having a go-to framework for your videos is helpful.

The Differences Between Fiction and Nonfiction Visual Storytelling

Before proceeding to the practical steps of visual storytelling, let's discuss the vital differences between crafting fiction and nonfiction stories. For most of us in ministry, our video stories are likely going to be nonfiction. Testimonies, ministry reports, event announcements, and sermon bumpers are all fairly straightforward to create, cheap to produce, and quick to record.

Most of the time, nonfiction videos will still require a script of some sort. Testimony videos can be scripted for B-roll after the testimony has been recorded and if the director knows what visuals will resonate with the interview.

There are a number of scripting software packages available for a price if you need to take you videos to that level. (If you have a drama ministry, this purchase could be beneficial to them and then the cost could be split between two budgets. Good stewardship at work!) Now without endorsing any of these, or getting into functionality reviews of one or another, I can say that Final Draft has been widely considered an industry standard, but comes with a little pricey. Others, some free, include:

- Highland

- Fade In

- Celtx

- Movie Magic

- Movie Draft

- Adobe Story

- Trelby

- Scrivener

There are also scripting templates and plug-ins for Microsoft Word. A simple Google search for these yields multiple possibilities for your usage.

Fiction is often tougher to produce because it must begin with a creative script—and most creative scripts are generally not that great. If they are, they're difficult to shoot effectively, cheaply, or quickly. Most churches don't have the resources and actors to pull off that type of video and make it compelling. (If your church is the exception to that rule, then my hat goes off to you. Way to go!)

I've made countless interview videos where our members simply tell their stories because our production time-frame was very short. Using talking heads with B-roll to give their story some life helps. While this is often one of the fastest ways to get a story told, it's not always the most effective or the most creative.

Taking their story and scripting it into a storytelling screenplay makes for a much more interesting video. This can be anything from video to still images to slideshows to animated graphics, which can be accompanied with catchy music or soft, inspirational music if the spot calls for it.

You don't necessarily have to have actors with dialog as a strong narrative can be more effective. (Actors with dialog better be great actors, especially in serious stories.) Narratives that tell the story while silent actors re-create the visuals seem to work great. To me, that's the perfect balance of technical efficiency: the story can be filmed well with just the right amount of time and effort put into it.

Regardless of the kind of video you're producing, our three guiding questions still apply. Always ask yourself these questions before creating any kind of visual story for your church. Again, these questions are:

Who is your audience?

What is the purpose of the video?

How long should the finished video be?

After answering those questions, you're ready to tackle producing your visual story.

4. Write your script.

Following a format for testimony videos maintains structure and keeps time limits under control. Our simplest format is:

- Introduce your subject.

- Bring in the conflict.

- Resolution.

- Celebration.

My pastor has sometimes asked me to split a testimony video in half for his sermon, with the introduction and conflict played before his message, and then the resolution and celebration played at the end of his sermon. We split it between Steps 2 and 3, which worked pretty well. We just had to put an ending on the first half and a beginning on the second half to make each part feel right. This kind of splitting works if the video testimony comes out a little longer and the pastor wants the longer story without cutting it down—and if he's willing to give up a few minutes of his speaking time.

If you're curious as to how long a written script might run when spoken, use a free online calculator, such as the one at

- http://www.speechinminutes.com.

If your speaker has a normal rate of speaking at 130 words-per-minute, you only have to write two hundred words for a two-minute spot, and that's assuming your speaker talks the entire time. While two hundred words might not seem like much, they need to be two hundred right words.

Both nonfiction and fiction videos produced for churches should stick to being short and without an abundance of dialogue. Scripting videos before shooting them will help ensure you meet both of those goals.

SIDE NOTE: What about unscripted testimony videos? How can you let a person share their heart while also ensuring your video doesn't run longer than one or two minutes?

Admittedly, this is hard to do in testimony videos when the person has a meaty testimony and you feel that every sentence is crucial. That's when proper editing becomes essential. If you're able to cut the video so it captures the overall tone of the person's story, they are usually happy with the outcome. They may say that you left out certain parts, but they also are usually understanding of your limitations, especially if you can say something to the effect of, "All of our testimony videos have to be less than two minutes." It wouldn't hurt to add the result of the video too, such as, "And I didn't see a dry eye in the church after it was finished."

5. Storyboard.

Basically, this is visualizing and drawing one picture of each section of script. It is a graphic realization of how you foresee the scene taking shape along with notes about what is happening and key lines that may be spoken in the scene.

For example, you want person walking their dog on the sidewalk, so you draw them head to toe on the left side with the leash going to the dog on the lower right while the camera tracks them on a dolly shot. This is obviously a simple example.

When you have more unusual camera angles or different framing techniques, storyboarding really helps to convey these ideas to the rest of your team in order to achieve your final vision.

Sometimes storyboarding is not always practical at the beginning. For a testimony video, you will probably wish to record the interview first, get the story down so that you know where the video is going. Then, in order to plan your B-roll, you storyboard from that. Draw a rectangular frame and sketch out how you see that shot looking based on the story that was told. A good interviewer will work to pull not only the good story from the person who has the impactful story, but will also be thinking visually as they go. While the story drives everything, the visuals help bring it home. How can the visuals help bring out the heart of the message that is being shared?

"The 'I do' scene, take thirty-six."

Image licensed through Stockphotos.com by Marty Hill and Quaddot Productions. Used by Permission.

6. Plan and check everything possible—EVERYTHING—before the camera rolls.

This is where you get to learn that there is no difference between being professionally detailed minded and really OCD! And there is absolutely nothing wrong with either in this case. Planning everything means everything in front and behind the camera. Leave no stone unturned. Scout your location. Know your set. Know your team. As much as possible, know your talent.

Map your scene. By mapping your scene I am referring to checking your camera shots for lighting of course, but also for everything else that is in the shot. There may be a really cool painting in the frame with text on it, but when your talent sits down on the set and blocks part of a word, the last thing you want is the part of the text that remains magically becomes PG-13 – or worse! Or maybe it's a book on the shelf doing the same thing. Or something else in the background doing something else that is distracting. Remove any and all distractions. The key point here is to CHECK THE BACKGROUND on all cameras!

Check your audio. Always monitor your audio through headphones as you record. Listen for pops, distortions, etc. Redo any parts that need redoing. Bad audio is a distraction and should not be used if at all possible. And always, always, always use brand new batteries.

In interviews, I never use tally lights. They distract the talent. Plus I usually start recording as soon as they sit down. I am able to get usable B-roll during this time plus some candid usable discussion on the topic at times if we should discuss the content while we are preparing. On many occasions, once they know we have started, many people that are not used to being on camera tense up and are not as free and easy. Therefore casual conversation often gives more natural responses. Just don't do anything uncool with this that loses their trust. I've never had any negative repercussions with this technique because every video I've ever done I've with the spirit of honoring the person whose story I'm telling. I'm working to tell their story the very best I can and I want them to be extremely happy with it.

7. Plan your shot list schedule deliberately.

When planning a video, the scope of the video will determine how you proceed.

A testimony video may not become clear as to how it flow until after the actual interview. You will have some initial ideas, but until you get the actual interview and learn firsthand what content you have to work with, you might not know exactly how the overflow will proceed.

However, you may have a good idea of some basic B-roll shots. You may know the story took place at a family's home and at a local hospital. You could actually already start collecting exterior b-roll shots of these locations if they are close by and time is on your side. Once the interview is completed, you will have a better idea of how the remaining B-roll and video will play out. Will the person or people who are the center of the story actually be the storytellers, or would it be better with a narrator, using the main talent for moments that only they can relate? How much B-roll and what kind of B-roll will be needed? Storyboarding these usually is a good idea, especially if you are asking someone else to go and shoot it.

Other video that is not testimony video can be more deliberate and planned out. It would be initially scripted, with shots defined, music planned out, and length of video known from the outset. With this, a shot list can be planned so that locations are only visited once. Maybe the beginning and ending of the 3-minute video are in the same location, but everything else is somewhere else. With that, you would shoot both the beginning and ending sequences at the same time to maximize resources. This especially works in nonfiction videos where there are many scenes between many locations. Shoot all of one location first, then the next location, then the next. Then you put them together in the editing room. Having someone following the script for flow and someone watching for continuity issues is also a good idea in these cases.

I wish more churches were able to create videos such as these, but illustration videos usually do not allow for that level of creativity or that much lead production time to achieve these, so these dramatic illustration videos are few and far between. Plus they are difficult to do on a quality level. But it is something to strive for if you are looking for something creative to try in the future.

8. Do Not Fear the Cutting Room Floor

The term "Cutting Room Floor" is a phrase left over from the old film days when film would literally be cut with razor blades and then be dropped to floor. It would then be out of the movie for good. It was really on the cutting room floor. While that technique is a thing of the past, the expression remains part of our lingo. However, to this day, the hardest thing to do in the editing room is still cutting things out.

Testimony videos get especially difficult because you know the entire story. You hear things about the story the rest of the congregation will never hear because you will leave it on the floor. How do you decide what you leave and what you don't?

Typically, if you have the production time, start with the entire story and start whittling down. Begin with defining the three sections of the video, the introduction where you introduce the talent and why they are there. The second section is usually building the conflict or problem that they were facing, then the third section the resolution. Section by section just whittle out those things that are obvious or possibly a repeat of something they had already said. Then you can work to get the over-all time to down to your target time.

Hard choices may have to be made at this point. Is that statement really important to final point of the story? Does it fill a gap or possibly just handle a sidebar? Stories often other stories intertwined with them. You have to decide how important those are to the over-all story. Somebody becoming a Christian because of a small group in your church is important, but is it important if that happened at a small group function and that function was a Christmas party? Maybe. Maybe not. Depending on the other facts surrounding it, you would have to decide. It may be just enough that just the group made an impact in their life. The fact that it was a Christmas party could be irrelevant and not take the 15-30 seconds they talk about that aspect of it.

I know that sounds minor, but when you get to certain level of editing, and you are literally looking for seconds, every one counts. Sometimes taking two or three unnecessary words out of a phrase in someone's audio behind some B-roll can save two seconds.

Also, when editing, make sure all your edits are smooth and actually work as intended. Avoid flashy edits unless you are editing a video that justifies it. I generally use cuts on fast moving videos and dissolves on slow or emotional ones. Cuts are generally considered the most powerful transition in video. Do not be afraid to use it. Watch your edits for those edit jumps before a transition is complete as well. Like a dissolve where a scene is fading out and the image changes to the next image on the recording before the dissolve is out. Or a cut that is too close to the end of the clip and actually gets one frame of the next scene before cutting. Review all transitions to make sure they are all clean.

Make sure speaking audio is balanced from one clip to the next. Nothing is more annoying than when one person is talking and the clip changes and the next person is significantly louder or softer. Also make sure music is properly balanced with the speaking as well.

9. Music.

Music can make or break a video. If the story is the heart of a video, the music is its soul. Music is the language that transcends the spoken word and reaches into our hearts and souls before the spoken word can be spoken, heard, and interpreted.

Music provides the feel of a video. It determines the speed of the edits and the subject's emotional temperament. When the person being interviewed is sad, the music ought to convey sadness too. Music can likewise foreshadow events turning toward the positive with a happier and more rhythmic sound.

Deciding on music early on in the editing process can actually help in the creative process. In a perfect world, this should actually be part of the scripting process back in step 4. While we spend so much time concentrating on video—the quality of the camera shot, its focus and color depth, the lighting, the crispness of the microphone quality, the actors, etc.—we tend to spend a fraction of time thinking about the music. How often do we just settle on some music because it will work just fine? If we reversed that and defined the music before we began editing (and maybe even before shooting the video), the end product could actually be something better than anything we'd done before because all of its elements would be cohesive!

10. Cataloging.

Finally, catalogue your final video and, if possible, your raw footage, for usage should the need ever arise. This becomes a valuable resource if it is needed again and can save you time having to re-shoot. B-roll shot but not used could come in handy on a different project. Footage on the testimony may prove invaluable for someone else when honoring them a few years later at another event in their life. And you would be the hero for having such footage around draw from to assemble such a great new video.

The pastor may wish to play that video once more because it was so effective the first time. Regardless, a good library system for your resources is a valuable tool to have and will prove itself again and again.

My final thought on the storytelling aspect of this part would be that stories are how people relate.

Pastors fill their sermons with them.

Television is full of them. That is what attracts us to it.

We go to theatre to watch plays because of the stories they present and movies for the same reason.

Everything is based on stories and storytelling.

We are a story-based culture whether we realize or not. Gossip, unfortunately, is all about stories. People who gossip just cannot wait to pass it on. That is a whole other topic, however! But it is still based in story.

I also must add that, and I'm sure someone has already thought this, Jesus Himself taught in story, also known as parable. He was the Master Storyteller!

Telling stories such as Roger Well's testimony, which was just a guy who thought he was living a good life, but his community came around him, showed him Christ, and let the Holy Spirit do the rest. That became a story which was told multiple times. Everyone has a story. Everyone. Someone just has to learn to ask the questions to uncover it. It may be simple or very painful and deep, but never discount on how that can be used by God.

Do not be afraid to be a storyteller.

Mastering the art of storytelling cannot be emphasized enough.

Go forward and learn more.

Watch continuously and study hard.

Practice and hone your skills and you can become a great minister in the area of storytelling for your church!

> "Tell me the facts and I'll learn.
> Tell me the truth and I'll believe.
> But tell me a story and it will live
> in my heart forever."
> An old Native American proverb

VIDEO STORYTELLING

REVIEW QUESTIONS

1. Why are stories a good resource to use in our services?

2. Discuss the difference between fictional and nonfiction storytelling and the strengths and weaknesses of each.

3. Discuss each of the ten essentials of video storytelling and why they are important.

4. How can you implement video storytelling in your ministry if you do not have the budget or manpower for a large production?

5. Do you know of stories in your congregation that would make good videos? How could those be produced even on a small scale?

CHAPTER 11

Backups Are Your Best Friend

I looked at my watch. Even though I was in Indianapolis to see my son march with the Blue Knights® of Drum Corp International®, I knew what was about to happen at my home church in Fort Worth. Our earliest Sunday service was minutes away from beginning and my phone was ringing.

"Marty, we have a problem."

"Tell me what's happening."

"Nothing is on the screens and the switcher and the lyric computer aren't working."

I shook my head and thought about airplanes. When I was working on obtaining my private pilot's license, it seemed as if 80 percent of what I was learning was how not to die. Maybe it's better put that I spent most of my time learning what to do in case of any kind of emergency. The remaining 20 percent of the time was filled with the basics of taking off, flying, and landing—which most people would think are the most important things to learn about flying. But those are the basics.

The logic of such teaching is that you must learn to handle emergencies before actual emergencies occur. Remaining ignorant about what to do when your plane experiences a significant problem will place both you and your passengers in jeopardy. A failure to plan is a plan to fail. Knowing what to do in any given situation dramatically increases your odds of a successful flight, even if something goes wrong.

That's why we spent so much time preparing for the worst, and that's why I thought about planes as I coached my volunteers through our backup plan.

Image licensed through Stockphotos.com by Marty Hill and Quaddot Productions. Used by Permission.

"What Happens If...?"

On a scale of one to ten, with one being "I've never thought about our backup plan" and ten being "I have backups of backups of backups," how would you rate your backup plan?

If you rated yourself as a five or less, you might be in the majority. Most tech ministers fail to create sufficient backup plans for lack of knowledge, time, resources, or money. But none of those issues should be a problem, because to go without a backup plan will someday mean losing time, resources, or money. In other words, what you fear losing today will likely be lost to a greater degree in the future due to a nonexistent or insufficient backup plan.

Ask yourself if a system went down right before a service or during a service, do you have a backup for that? If not a backup system, at least do you have a backup plan? Have you played a little game I like to call, "What happens if...?" You look at each and every system, and maybe even elements inside those systems, and ask yourself if that dies or malfunctions, what is Plan B... or Plan C? If you were ever a Boy Scout this goes back to the Boy Scout motto of "Be Prepared." We always strive for excellence, but, again, as when I was learned taking pilot lessons, we have to plan for the worst, so that we are ready if and when it happens .

Additionally, creating and maintaining proper backups requires discipline and consistency. Wouldn't it be nice if your backup processes were built into your regular regimen? If you follow the general guidelines presented in this chapter, creating sufficient, predictable, and practical backup processes can be done with little to no special effort.

All you need is to set aside dedicated time to consider your church's particular needs for backing up all software processes and all hardware needs. I'm also fully aware that most churches can't just buy two of every hardware device so that they always have a full backup. I'll provide tips and workarounds so that any church can at least make it through that inevitable Sunday morning crisis that always seems to happen at the worst possible time—like when you're thousands of miles away and only have ten minutes to get everything working before the service starts.

Software Backup Tips

Compared to backing up hardware, backing up your ministry's software is definitely the easier process, but it still requires forethought. In today's technical society, cost-effective software backup options abound, from flash drives to cloud-based storage to local servers to RAIDs. What you use is a preferential decision, but give thought to the reason why you're choosing one option over another.

Remember: while you can create your own scripts or set your software to create backups automatically, most of your backups will be conducted manually. This helps ensure that you're being intentional about the backups you're creating. Otherwise, if you rely on automation, you may not actually have the backup you need at the time you need it. Murphy's Law will undoubtedly raise its ugly head: "Anything that can go wrong, will go wrong," especially ten minutes before a worship service. Without a routine backup process in place, your one-and-only working lyric file may become corrupted, leaving you with zero options for a quick replacement.

This is not a fun time around the tech booth. (And if you've been in technical ministry for long enough, you don't need me to remind you of that!)

Here's one backup solution that has been used for lyric files:

- Create lyrics, slides, and sermon presentations on a single office computer.

- Copy and paste that file into Dropbox (dropbox.com), a cloud-based storage program that's free up to two gigabytes of storage.

- Be sure to have Dropbox installed on every computer where those files are needed and that every user of those computers who needs to access those files knows the tech ministry's Dropbox login credentials.

- Copy and paste the Dropbox file onto the presentation computer's hard drive.

NOTE: A word which is getting ahead of Chapter 13, Dropbox is just one current solution in 2017. As technologies develop, grow with them. There are many others, and more will continue to arrive with new capabilities. Do not be afraid to use these. Again, be resourceful and innovative, but above all, have a backup system!

By using the presentation computer's local copy, we had two other copies of that file in case of an emergency: the file on Dropbox and the file on the original office computer. Note: just be sure not to drag the file out of Dropbox else you're effectively deleting that file from your Dropbox account—and consequently from every computer that relies on Dropbox for access to that file. (But even if that happens, if you follow the guidelines above, you'll still have that first created copy—a master file—on your office computer's local storage.)

Other than our normal preparations for a Sunday worship service, no extra work was required for such a quick, easy, and inexpensive software backup solution which gave us two backups.

While it's always smart to devise your own manual backup systems, you should also stay up-to-date on the programs your ministry uses. For instance, ProPresenter offers its own cloud-syncing capabilities to ensure its files work across multiple computers. Even with such a solution, I'd still recommend building redundancies like our Dropbox solution. USB hard drives, Network drives, anything that can serve as a mirrored drive and a backup will be your best friend.

Hardware Backup Tips

Planning when and how to backup your hardware will require extra research and time on your part and isn't usually seriously considered given the extra expense it sometimes creates. But implementing a working solution will make you look like a genius when crunch time threatens (However, don't forget the humility factor!)

"That's usually not a good sign."

Image licensed through Stockphotos.com by Marty Hill and Quaddot Productions. Used by Permission.

1. Know your systems.

Know what each component can do whether you're using that feature or not. Many pieces of gear have multiple outputs. If one output dies, another may still work. Or, if you're sending a 1080p signal to your projector and your image doesn't appear, know where the 720p settings are on your switcher and your projector. The video may work fine on that setting.

2. Fight for your backup needs.

If you use multiple computers to control different screens, try to make sure you can reroute any computer to any screen. A good digital router system is the best way to do this. Unfortunately, such routers are generally expensive, and it can be hard to convince a ministry leader why you need it. They might ask, "You need a box that does nothing I can see or hear and costs how much?"

Most of the time it's easier to lift a glacier over your head than convince them of this need, but if it becomes a recurring issue, you'll have more fuel for your argument. It's also easier to argue for if your church is in "building mode" and the overall budget has enough room to add a digital router.

3. Make the best use of what you have or can afford.

If you don't have a digital router, you still have options. This is another reason to know your gear and all its ports. Extra ports can often give you backup options you may not always think of except in crisis situations.

If and when you buy a new switcher, purchase a switcher with auxiliary outputs. This can be made to serve as a router. Using AUX channels in the role of a router can be a lifesaver.

If you don't have a digital router or an AUX-filled switcher, one of the cheapest options is a wired patch bay. Since this involves unplugging and plugging in patch cables, this solution isn't pretty when changes must be made while projectors are running. In fact, I highly discourage such changes during a program. But patch bays do allow for rerouting signals as needed before an event begins.

If you just need to reroute up to four sources to a destination, the absolute cheapest solution is a composite switch box from your local electronics supply store. Remember: signal types have to match. You cannot send an analog signal to a digital destination or vice-versa. You will not want to send a composite signal to a piece of gear expecting a component signal. Switch boxes cost usually begin in the $15–$50 range and go up, but, at those prices, the end result might not be the quality you want. But they can sometimes get you by in a pinch.

Like working with patch bays, you shouldn't change anything on a switch box while an image is on-screen. It won't be pretty. Switch boxes are a last-resort solution, and I only recommend it for getting out of a jam or for a one-time use. This is not a professional solution, but when in a crunch, whatever makes something work how you need it to work, then that's the correct solution for the moment.

If you're not already incorporating this type of planning into your thinking, I highly recommend it. Always think about what your backups are if a principle system fails. If possible, build it in place. You'll be glad you did!

4. Plan for worst-case scenarios.

This brings us back to the problem my team was having with the lyric computer when I was thousands of miles away. First, they had to get at least something to show up on the screens. Because we had a digital router system in place, I instructed them as to which output controlled the signal to the projectors. By changing the input source to that output, they were essentially using the router as a switcher. Of course, everything would be cuts only, meaning there would be no dissolves, no keying, etc., but the service could go on, and a vast majority of the congregation would be unaware of any difference. Problem one solved.

Problem two was the lyric computer. After some quick, over-the-phone troubleshooting, I decided to go with that computer's backup option. We had a second computer that was primarily used to record the message for web playback. Since we also recorded the entire service to digital tape, we sacrificed the web video knowing we could later recover it. When we had installed that second computer, we'd anticipated the possibility of the eventual need for a backup, so we'd installed the lyric program on it as well.

Sort of.

5. Don't forget the details.

When my volunteers launched the lyric program, a message popped up: "Your demo period has expired." It might as well have just said, "Murphy's Law strikes again. LOL." Some goober—me—had never fully installed the program with its unlock key. As I heard my team sigh over the phone, I pulled up the unlock key I'd stored in my smartphone's notes.

6. Take responsibility.

Now the problem was time. I could have walked my volunteers through the procedure, or I could have done what I felt would be faster in that situation. I opted for the latter, and maybe because I felt guilty for the unlock key issue. I logged in remotely from my laptop, set the unlock key, pulled the playlist up for them, and double-checked everything. As soon as they got that computer's signal routed to the screens, everything was fine—right as the band started their first song! If I'd walked the volunteers through all of those steps, they likely would have missed at least the first song.

7. Plan for failure.

Backups and remote access saved my bacon that day. You may plan for many backups you'll never use. However, you'll plan for backups that reward your efforts the first time they're needed. I'd rather have experienced the near-failures I talked about in this chapter much more than experiencing total failures without backups.

Planning and creating backups is like purchasing insurance. No one likes spending money or time on something they may never use, but when you need it, you're so glad you made such an investment. When problems inevitably arise and your backups aren't in place, it's too late. By investing now, you'll be rewarding yourself and your team later.

The silent reward is that when you need the backup, it kicks in without the congregation knowing anything had ever gone wrong. Others on your team will know, and your stock in their eyes will grow. (Again, remember the whole humility thing.)

The importance of backups cannot be overstated. For software backups, you might have a little more work and maybe some expenses you wouldn't have had otherwise. For hardware backups, you may need to acquire a few more pieces of gear (and definitely more cables), and you will likely spend more money. Thinking through your hardware backup solutions will also require spending time in thought about your church's specific needs.

And, finally, let me say, that there will be times that something will happen that there was absolutely no way you could have anticipated it. In this case, because you have so over-prepared for everything else, you have your poise and training to rely on to give you peace in the knowledge that you can handle it, thinking it through calmly, isolate the problem, come up the best resolution and implement it in such a way that your team has the same calmness around you and performs admirably as well, following the example of their leader, you.

Also, some resolutions may require totally out-of-the-box solutions. No solution is wrong if it works. There may always be better answers you may think about later, but whatever works in the moment, no matter how crazy, is fine. One example would be that a prop has one of four short legs collapse. It is broken. The prop is useless without that leg. If you had time, you would repair the leg. But time is not on your side. You have one minute until the service begins. Your solution? You prop it up with a number of old hymnbooks that are still hanging around from days of yore and cover it with black fabric. (How many of us have used hymn books for uses such as this and it not be an emergency?) That is a fairly simple outside-of-the-box example. There are certainly countless more extreme ones. Just don't be afraid to do whatever it takes, no matter what to get through the moment. It may not feel professional at the time, but if it saves the day, and the congregation is unaware, that is all that matters. A true professional, in my opinion does whatever it takes to rescue the moment.

Remember: you're piloting your team through every weekend worship service. As a pilot, you need to be prepared for every emergency. If you have your backup solutions in place long before you'll ever have to make an emergency landing, then you'll know exactly what needs to be done when some piece of equipment begins to malfunction.

Then you can LOL right back into Murphy's face.

BACKUPS ARE YOUR BEST FRIEND

REVIEW QUESTIONS

1. Ask yourself if a system went down right before a service or during a service, do you have a backup for that?

    - If not a backup system, at least a backup plan?

    - Have you played, "What happens if...?"

2. Do you have examples of when a backup in place saved the day for your ministry on a weekend?

    - Discuss this.

    - What was learned from it?

3. Do you have and example when there was NOT a backup in place and one was implemented as a result of a weekend crash?

    - Discuss this.

    - Why did it take the crash to implement this backup?

CHAPTER 12

IMAG, Checklists, etc.

This may seem elementary, but I've been surprised by how many do not fully understand the topic of IMAG. If you don't know what IMAG stands for, you're not alone, but now you'll know: IMAG is an acronym for Image MAG-nification. In layman's terms for churches, it's using projectors and screens, LED walls, or other large-screen methods to show live video during a worship service or other event. You're basically using cameras to significantly magnify what the audience can see, and that simple fact should help you assess whether your church needs IMAG or not.

If you've been in technical ministry for a number of years, one of three things is possible:

- You're already doing IMAG and have a good grasp of it but would like to learn some new things or just hone up on the basics. If that's the case, jump to the section a few pages ahead titled, "Shoot for the live congregation first," and read from there.

- You're doing a lot of great things but not IMAG.

- Your church's technical ministry is fairly new and you're trying to decide if you should do IMAG.

Consider this: Do you serve at a large church where the people in the back can barely tell who's preaching? Or do you want to use IMAG because it seems everyone else is doing it, even though your church sits a hundred people on a good day?

If "Jeff Foxworthy" style, here are some general rules of thumb when choosing whether IMAG is necessary for your church:

- If your attendance is less than three hundred people and the farthest person from the stage is fifty feet or less away, you don't need IMAG.

- If your camera shot makes the person smaller on screen than with the human eye, you don't need IMAG.

- If your church cannot afford the investment of the equipment that is required to start and maintain this, you don't need IMAG.

- If the video quality is poor, you don't need IMAG.

- If manning a team overly stresses the few volunteers that you have to do this, you don't need IMAG.

- If you are doing this ONLY because it is the trend of day and all the other churches are doing it, you don't need IMAG.

These not a hard and fast rules. Different rooms and different congregations define different needs, so use your judgment.

One the first point, that three hundred person number can be as high as eight hundred in another building. Distance from stage is more often the determining factor. But all of these hopefully will provide you with some things to consider before implementing IMAG.

If you're starting from scratch, many companies can assist you in the design and installation of a complete IMAG system. However, starting from absolutely nothing can be an expensive project, and so much so that most churches include new IMAG systems as part of a larger giving campaign. However, if you already have projectors and screens in place because you're already projecting lyrics and graphics for the congregation, part of the battle is already won. Now, you just have to add the video portion. This is still expensive, but at least part of the infrastructure is already in place.

In such a setup, you'll need to evaluate cameras, switchers, and anything else that might be required for your existing system to get live video onto your screens. Meet with your local AV rep, explain your goals and budget, and they will make informed recommendations. Get at least three bids to make sure you're getting the best result for your church's investment. Different companies often deal with different hardware, so you may find you like one package better than another based on that. Prices may vary significantly as well, which is certainly another important factor in whom you choose.

As far as specs go, you must consider these two primary needs:

ASPECT RATIO

For basic IMAG, today's normal aspect ratio is 16:9. Any other aspect ratio would call for stretching, squishing, or cropping the image to fit inside the screen. Keeping to 16:9 eliminates headaches down the line. Fight the urge to be creative and do something out of the norm, like super-wide or odd-shaped screens. While there are really cool ways to pull these off and they work great for special touches or other special effects on stage, they are generally not recommended for IMAG. Now, if someone comes up with a cool solution that works outside of the 16:9 ratio and isn't a regular headache for the crew or production staff, then congratulations! Go to the head of the creative class! But, for the norm, keep to 16:9 until such a day comes that the industry standard changes to some other ratio.

RESOLUTION – 1080p, 720p or 4K?

Let's face it: there aren't too many IMAG displays that can handle 4K yet, and the hardware on the backside to support 4K is even less in place. Setups with 4K cameras, switches, and everything else in between just aren't practical yet. So let's rule that one for now. 1080p is fine if the entire system is tuned for it and the graphics computers and video playback systems are set up for and can handle 1080p. In reality, most large-room venues today use 720p because the visual difference on screen between 720p and 1080p is negligible. Additionally, 720p streams place a lesser burden on computers and other systems than 1080p streams, resulting in better system reliability.

If your church is large enough that IMAG will prove helpful, consider these tips.

1. Shoot for the live congregation first.

The foremost reason for using IMAG is to help your audience better see those on the stage. Facial expressions are as much a part of a speaker's delivery as is their tone of voice. The same is true for worship leaders. Seeing faces helps communicate more than just the words we hear.

That's why IMAG-using churches must shoot for the live audience first and magnify what they can't already see. For instance, a head-to-toe camera shot that makes the speaker the same size on the screen as he is to the eye is no help at all. Such a shot is often used because the IMAG video signal is being recorded for web or DVD playback. In that case, what's the point of even having IMAG when it's not magnifying anything?

If you're relegated to having only one video feed for multiple uses, one use will have to take precedent over the others. Use IMAG for its intended purpose. Shoot for the live congregation first and make all other purposes secondary. After all, an

Internet- or DVD-viewer won't mind the close-ups. And besides, those in attendance at the service actually got up, got dressed, and came to the service!

If you have the benefit of a multi-feed system, you can use one feed for the live service and send another feed, complete with camera changes and cuts, to a recording device. The most direct route to implement such a system is to use two switchers with two directors. You can also consider using a 2 M/E switcher as two switchers instead of just using it for multiple effects: 1 M/E is for your screens and the other is for recording. (Just make sure your video director in this position is highly attentive and doesn't suffer from A.D.D.)

2. Seek feedback.

Before using IMAG for the first time, talk to your pastor(s) and worship leader(s) about how they envision IMAG being used during the service. For instance, does your pastor want full-screen graphics during his message, or does he prefer to always have live video with any graphics overladen on the lower-third of the screen?

It may be even more important to get feedback from a worship pastor. Do they want full-screen video all the time with lower-third lyrics? Do they want to cut from full-screen lyrics to live video and back again? Will they be relying on IMAG for lyrics? (That's a dangerous choice, by the way!)

Some worship leaders don't like to see themselves on screen because they say it puts emphasis on them rather than on the Lord. But others believe it helps make them better worship leaders and allows the emotions of the moment to be better conveyed, especially to a large audience. Both of these reasons are why you need to talk to your worship leader and discover where they stand on such an issue. Then work with them to find the right balance between honoring their request and serving your congregation.

3. Know your timing.

A video director must always think ahead. They have to know when a video follows the third song in a set, and as soon as that third song begins, the video is ready to go.

A camera director should know every part of every song. If the band repeats the chorus eight times and hits the bridge twice, the camera director should be singing right along— maybe not literally, but in their mind.

An experienced camera director will also know their worship leaders' habits. For instance, if a worship leader turns to give the band direction with hand signals, a camera director will cut away from the worship leader and show another member of the band.

Camera directors should likewise always be able to anticipate an upcoming guitar solo or know that the alto is going to be the lead singer on the fifth song. They should be cueing up the shot before the shot is needed. How many times have you heard an instrumental solo begin while you're still watching the lead singer sway and hum, or see a camera operator cut to a soloist just as their solo is done?

A good director knows every song's arrangement, every camera's placement, every next shot needed, and switches to that shot just before the first note is sung or played. Late transitions distract. Quality productions dispense with distractions so that churches can worship in spirit and truth.

There's more to this than just knowing the worship leader and their songs. Knowing the pastor's speaking style, how much he moves while onstage, and learning to read his body language is very important in being able to direct your camera shots during the sermon. While your pastor may follow his sermon notes word-for-word to the point that it's a script more than notes, that won't always alert you that he may move left or right, or sit down on a stool, or stand up from one.

By watching and studying his body language, you can begin to anticipate most of his major movements. You may notice his shoulders slowly start to rotate toward the left a few seconds before he fully turns and takes a few steps that way. Or, if he's sitting on a stool, you may notice that he starts to slightly lean forward before he finally decides to stand up. Then, when he later does these major moves, you're ready with your camera operator to track with him.

Or, you'll know to switch to another camera with a wider shot to fully capture the entire shift in direction. This body language strategy can and should apply to anyone who regularly appears onstage. As you get to know them, tracking with them becomes almost second-nature.

Regarding props, ensure that any props are set up on stage early, the lighting is planned, camera angles are tested, and the stage placement is spiked once settled. Preferably, the pastor will be involved or informed at some point so that he knows where to stand with these considerations in mind. Then, when these props are used inside the sermon, your cameras and lights are all set ahead of time. You or your camera director can follow the pastor's notes and will be ready for the prop when its use comes. There will be no surprises. Your timing will be on the mark, making your pastor's sermon as technically perfect as possible.

4. Be patient with your team (especially volunteers).

Remember that you may be working with volunteer directors who've never done this type of work before. They likely haven't worked for a local TV station or a video production company. And while they may be familiar with video equipment, shooting live video and producing a service in real time is a new and different challenge that they'll have to overcome with consistent experience—and your patience.

Use any failures as a way to teach them what went wrong and how they could ensure it doesn't happen again.

5. If IMAG doesn't enhance worship, eliminate it.

Lastly, even if your church is large enough to merit using IMAG, you may need to consider eliminating its use if it creates more distractions than it removes. As with all technology we bring to bear upon a worship service, IMAG ought to enhance a worship experience. Once it becomes a distraction, the effect you were hoping to achieve with its use disappears.

But, used correctly and wisely, IMAG can enhance your worship |so that it becomes even more anointed, touching, and able to change lives.

Here is a pretty good link for you to check out for as long as it is up that presents some basic IMAG setup:

https://worshipimag.com/installation-pictures/
simple-imag-system/

CHECKLISTS AND RESOURCES

A technical minister needs equal parts technical knowledge and ministerial leanings to perform their job to the best of their abilities. That knowledge comes from experience, a drive to always keep learning, and the ability to find and effectively use the right resources. With technology always changing, we have to always be watching and learning. It never ends. If we stop researching and learning new things, we will be left behind and our days will be numbered.

I offer this chapter as a clearinghouse of helpful resources for technical ministers. While it's not comprehensive in terms of presenting all your available options, it is comprehensive with regard to my recommendations for a variety of areas that technical ministers need to know and understand.

First, we'll start with a resource that's so basic it's just ink on paper, but it's so integral that I believe every technical minister needs to implement its use.

Check In with Checklists

When I took lessons for my private pilot's license, checklists were always emphasized. Each plane had its own checklist specific to its make and model. Walking through your checklist was of paramount importance. After all, missing one item could cost your life and the lives of your passengers, not to mention maybe the lives of people on the ground.

Consequently, I was strictly taught to walk through the checklist every time I flew. I could never assume that all would go according to plan on a present flight because I hadn't had issues on a previous flight. So, I diligently adhered to these checklists. On every flight, I walked through each item and checked them off one by one.

Of course, meticulously going over such a thorough checklist took time. I couldn't just hop on a plane, start the engine, taxi to the runway, and take off. I had to set time aside to prepare myself for the flight ahead—every time. The temptation to skip the checklist procedure, either out of boredom or hurry, can be alluring. But even skimming the list can easily lead to carelessly overlooking what could prove to be crucial to a successful flight.

I thought about this invaluable lesson when I finally incorporated checklists into our tech team's routine. It took a little time to implement, but the end results were well worth it. Unfortunately, I didn't implement checklists until after our team had been missing certain things they would have otherwise caught—with the help of a checklist.

On multiple instances, our countdown clocks didn't work, or didn't appear on our production computer, or failed to show up on the correct output screen. Sometimes we played the wrong version of a video, or cut it off too soon. Certainly, these weren't life-or-death mistakes, but they were distracting issues that could have been rectified by the simple use of a checklist.

Every position had its own checklist. We also created general pre-worship and post-worship checklists. (In the Chapter 15, the Resources chapter, you will find links as to where you can download samples of some of these.) The post-worship checklist included items like: save the files, close all programs, turn off all monitors, place the wireless headset battery on its charger, and clean the counter of paper and unnecessary items. The checklist even has "Dust all equipment" so that we could maintain a clean environment.

Unsurprisingly, our effective increased as our mistakes decreased, which has the better effect of boosting morale across your team and your staff. After all, we are the church staffers who are often only noticed when something goes wrong!

After the checklists had been created and refined, we printed them on card stock paper and laminated them to lengthen their life. When minor changes were implemented, we used a permanent marker and wrote the change on the checklist. If more than a few such changes were made, we edited, reprinted, and re-laminated it.

It will take time to get your checklists created and refined, but once you have final checklists in place and your team begins using them, you'll wonder why you didn't create them sooner.

Once your team gets used to using your checklists, you'll still have to make sure they actually use them. They need to know that they can't just run through them from memory or rush through them because they're hurried. Remember the flying analogy. When they begin checking out on using the checklist, little mistakes will creep in. Then bigger mistakes will appear, and then they'll be embarrassed because they'll have to admit that they didn't follow the checklist, which would have rectified the mistake that got by them.

To help get your wheels turning, links to a few checklists are included in the resource section at the end of this book. Feel free to use and adapt these to your situation.

Plan Well with Cue Sheets

Whether you call them cue sheets, worship orders, or run sheets, their purposes are the same: to set and maintain the flow of a worship service.

These sheets may be as simple or complex as you want them to be. I suggest that the more complex your service is, the more simplified your cue sheet should be. Cue sheets can also be customized for each position. After all, the lighting tech doesn't need to know that the baptism graphic goes up next. But don't go overboard and feel that you have to make individual cue sheets all the time for every position. In all instances, I recommend this:

> The KISS strategy:
> Keep It Simple, Sam!

I highly recommend using Planning Center Online (PCO: planningcenteronline.com) to create your cue sheets. PCO has a monthly cost based on the number of members in your church, but it's a great resource for planning your services and scheduling your teams. The ability to create custom reports is a cool feature if you have someone who drools over programming. PCO's flexibility is great, and they're always working to make it better, add features, and provide in-depth support through training materials and webinars so you can use it to the fullest according to your needs.

For those without money to spend on a monthly subscription to PCO, or for those who want even more flexibility than what PCO offers (though it's certainly been flexible enough for our needs), the cost-effective alternative is planning your worship service in an Excel spreadsheet. In some ways, that's more tedious than planning in PCO, but a spreadsheet does allow you to accomplish some things that PCO does not, like highlighting people, places, items, etc. in different colors. (I wouldn't be surprised to see PCO add this in the future, but at the time of this writing, it's not a function of their website application.)

Schedule Better with a Calendar Spreadsheet

Speaking of spreadsheets, I've used a massive spreadsheet for years as my yearly Worship Calendar. I can't take credit for its origin, but I have adapted it over the years as needed and I'm so glad to have it.

My Worship Calendar is a Microsoft Excel workbook and has multiple tabs, each of which corresponds to one calendar year. On each tab, we track a number of things that are integral to our worship services. The beauty is that after you've been doing it for a few years, it's simple to see what you've done in the past to plan for the future.

For instance, when Christmas Eve fell on Sunday, we wondered how we had handled that situation years earlier. By looking at the tab for that year, we saw if we'd had our three morning services in addition to our three or four candlelight services.

For that weekend years ago, our review notes said, "Next time consider not doing the morning services in exchange for the candlelight services. Staff and volunteers exhausted." So we canceled the morning services in exchange for the candlelight services and our staff rejoiced.

I've also used our Worship Calendar to find the exact date of a service, such as a special children's event, so that someone wanting a DVD of that service receives the right recording. The possibilities that open up as a result of tracking your services for years on end are many, but they're also directly related to how much information you choose to track.

These items could be tracked:

- Date

- Special Day (holidays, etc.)

- Sermon Series Title

- Sermon Series Subtitle

- Message Title

- Scripture Reference

- Speaker's Name

- Worship Leader's Name

- Host's Name

- Producer's Name

- Elder's Name

- Video Campus

- Special Announcements

- Special Touches (video, drama, etc.)

- Notes

- Review Notes

Some of these are obvious, like Special Day and Speaker's Name. Some are specific to our needs, like Video Campus. Since we had recently become a multi-site campus, we needed to track which of our two campuses would play back the video of the message. We attempted to evenly distribute the workload between both campuses, and tracking this item helped us do that. The Video Campus column named the campus and totaled the count, such as 24/25, meaning that we'd played video at one campus twenty-four times and twenty-five times at the other.

The Host is the person, usually a pastor, who welcomes the congregation, makes announcements, and leads communion and so forth. The Host does nearly everything but lead music and give the message.

Special Announcements are those that need to be brought to the congregation's attention with a verbal word. Special Touches are elements in the worship service such as creative videos, dramas, readings, and special songs. Basically, they're anything creative that will help drive the thematic element of the morning.

Besides just tracking history, we also set up the year's spreadsheet for advanced planning. We would highlight holidays, daylight savings time changes, spring breaks, and more so that we could plan accordingly. As we learned about them, we would also notate major events in the church that might affect a Sunday morning, such as a women's retreat.

Under Notes we would enter Sundays when a team member might be on vacation, a missionary might be in town, etc. Review Notes were entered during our debrief meeting the week following the event and used for future reference—like when Christmas Eve falls on a Sunday.

As you can tell, such a document can prove to be valuable over time. It takes a while for the looking-back part to kick in, but the planning part reaps instant rewards.

And remember: back up this file! You don't want to lose years of tracking!

Incorporate Video

Technology has advanced to the point where consumer-level equipment quality is very good and very affordable. Plus, many video-production hobbyists now own very powerful cameras and tripods. And it seems that every new smartphone release increases its video capture quality. With such cameras in the hands of many people in our congregations and on our church equipment lists, many churches are producing their own personalized videos for their congregations.

Using amateurs is great for reports on retreats, potluck dinners, video announcements, etc. The downside is that the camera operator likely isn't a trained videographer or a professional video editor who truly knows the business and art of video production, so the end product is not as refined as you'd want. However, for many of these types of videos, high-end production isn't necessary. But there are some times where quality is an issue and other resources can come into play.

If your church doesn't have the resources to produce your own high-quality videos, you can find a wide variety of videos for your use in a number of places online. These videos were created by different kinds of professional producers such as churches with pro-level resources, production houses that support ministries, or even just freelancers.

With churches that produce videos, many will make their videos available via their websites. Or, if you see their video online and you know what church created it, you can always call them to seek permission and high-resolution versions of the video if you cannot purchase that video directly on their website. This approach can often work for production houses and individuals as well.

To get their videos in front of as many eyes as possible and to earn money on what they create, many producers use online distributors such as:

- SermonSpice.com

- WorshipHouseMedia.com

- Ignitermedia.com

- Gracewaymedia.com

Producers have contracts with these sites and split earnings with them. Prices on these sites are generally pretty cheap. At the time of this writing, a good two- to three-minute illustration video is in the fifteen- to twenty-dollar range. Considering the actual cost of producing videos, this is a great deal. Producers hope to recoup their expenses in quantity and hopefully make some profit to support their ministries or businesses.

Building your own video production team is easier today than ever. The real questions become how often will you be making videos and at what quality of video will you be expecting? The answers to these will dictate your investment into this arena. If you are just planning an occasional video, such as a fun video report on a student ministry retreat, or a promo for an upcoming event, then a small volunteer team with minimal consumer equipment might actually suffice. But if the expectations and frequency are greater, then quality of equipment and skills of the video team go up in a hurry and their role in the church in order to achieve these objectives.

Cameras, tripods, lighting, microphones, cables, are just the tip of the iceberg for the gear needed for a serious video shoot.

The more complex the location or expectations, the higher the quality of equipment is usually needed as well as the skills to know how to properly use it. The main thing is to define your objective for video and then plan your best way to achieve that. Is it buying pre-produced videos from online resources, producing your own videos with volunteers, or developing a video production department and diving into a whole new world of creativity? The cool thing is that we live in a time with possibilities that no one before us in church history has been able to have. We can tell stories in a visual form that literally comes to life and can theoretically remain to be viewed for generations to come long after we've gone!

Pay Attention to Graphic Design

Graphic design is similar to video production. Prices have also come down in this area, and a lot of online graphics enable churches to create their own graphics as needed.

Unfortunately, there seems to be a trend of those who just Google what they need, find an image, and copy-and-paste it into their publication without concern for copyright. This is truly the wrong way to do things, and especially for a church, which should be above reproach. Dozens if not hundreds of affordable sites exist from which you can legally purchase photos and clipart. Some even offer a certain number of free graphics, but be careful how you use them: they may have certain license restrictions.

For stock photos, check out:

- Istockphoto.com

- Shutterstock.com

- Stockphoto.com

- Stock.adobe.com

- Fotolia.com

- Pond5.com

For free stock photos, check out:

- Pexels.com

- Pixabay.com

- Freestockphotos.com

For clipart, check out:

- Clipart.com

- Openclipart.com

- 1001FreeDownloads.com

It is important here to emphasize regardless of where you get your images, read your license to make sure the it covers how you intend to use it. Do not assume that just because you purchased the image that covers all possibles uses. Sometimes different uses need different licenses, and therefore, different fees. Again, stay above reproach and purchase the correct license for your usage.

If you wish to create quality graphics from scratch, you'll need a skilled graphic artist. The difference they'll make to what you create is night and day. You'll get exactly what you want with an originality you won't find by looking at online graphic available for purchase.

But the difference is in cost. Can your church afford another salaried position, or even just a contract freelancer from time to time? You will have to weigh the importance of that expense. It may be a contract for a one-time giving campaign where you request a bunch of similar graphics, or you hire them full-time for every graphic need in the church. This is preferred, but only if you have the budget for it. Employing a dedicated graphics design guru is truly worth the expense if you have the right person in the position.

Make the Most of Campus Video Monitors

Campus video monitors, i.e., screens placed in different areas of your church, can be used for multiple purposes. Their basic purpose is communication throughout the building, but they can be used in multiple ways depending on what you're communicating and to whom you want to communicate.

For instance, during services campus monitors can be used for the following purposes depending on their locations:

- Lobby Monitors: displays the service.

- Backstage: displays the service time clock along with a reference camera in order to keep everybody backstage who's involved with the service in sync with what's occurring onstage.

- Children's Ministry: displays messages pertinent to ministry staff volunteers and parents, such as remaining check-in time, time remaining in the worship service, the current time, upcoming events, video announcements for children, etc.

During the week, if there's a lot of traffic in the building, I like to leave the monitors on with looping, rotating announcements. It gives the building a feeling of continuous action and life. It also helps communicate information in those announcements just a little bit more. You never know how God might use such an announcement in a person's life!

Have a Proven System for Child and Nursery Alerts

Alert systems are now common in churches as at least a few children always need their parents at some point during a service or event. Many churches have moved to a texting system, which is less expensive to implement than some options. I believe that's the best option because pretty much everyone has a phone these days.

However, the drawback is that parents essentially have to be trained to have their cell phones always handy in case their child needs them. Sometimes the texting system fails because the parent's phone may be on silent, they don't feel its vibration, they forget to bring it to church, or the battery's dead. In this case, a backup system is highly recommended. Providing that kind of multi-level help is just good "customer service." By giving a number to a child and that parent, a production team can simply flash that number onto their LED wall or key it over whatever is already on-screen.

More expensive check-in and security solutions are available, but I recommend going with what works best for your particular church. Consider the texting option first, but be sure to have other options in mind if texting creates more problems than it solves.

Stream and Record Services

Having an Internet presence is so easy these days it's almost ridiculous. The importance of a church website is no longer debated. However, what needs to be on the website and how to lay out your information is always under scrutiny.

Bridgelelement.com conducted a study of websites on their servers, and the first thing they discovered was a 30 percent spike in traffic on Sunday mornings. And, 52 percent of those visitors were first-time visitors.[16] People are searching for church!

The Bridge Element study also found that the most visited page on any church website is the media page with pre-recorded sermons . Gone are the days of experiencing a sermon once and never hearing it again. A pastor can speak a sermon in a small room with fifty people and change the lives of countless people online. With streaming, live events are easily attended by those hundreds and thousands of miles away. Walls and roads are no longer barriers. If your church is online, consider recording and streaming your services, if not the whole service, then at least the teaching. If you're not streaming, at least archive your messages for playback.

When the idea of streaming first started coming around, the argument I came up against was that it would keep people from coming to church. While that may be true for a small percentage, I think the opposite is actual reality. In fact, in "Should Your Church Use Live Stream?," a Churchleaders.com interview by Greg Atkinson with Steve Lacy, founder and president of StreamingChurch.tv, Lacy[17] states that a key reason to stream live is church growth. He credits his church's quadrupling in regular attendance over two years to live streaming .

16   http://bridgeelement.com/blog/3-things-visitors-love-to-see-in-church-websites.php
17   http://churchleaders.com/outreach-missions/outreach-missions-blogs/145391-interview-with-steve-lacy-of-streamingchurch-tv.html

Live streaming now is simpler than ever. The only issue is quality. The less you spend on lighting, cameras, audio, computers, bandwidth, etc., the lower the quality will be on the user's end, which will reflect on your ministry. Keep that in mind as you plan.

Copyright is also an issue, especially with songs, though it will also matter to non-original videos, graphics, cartoons, etc. shown during your services. Any copyrighted materials must have streaming rights secured. These are separate from

- Christian Copyright Licensing International (CCLI)

- Church Video License CVLI

and other blanket copyright licenses that cover everything played in your worship center.

If the copyright license of an item in question fails to cover Internet streaming when purchased or otherwise acquired, you will have to contact the publisher, producer, creator, etc. to secure permission to record and/or stream the copyrighted material. Many times, it's just a formality, and only proper on-screen credit will be necessary, if that. Sometimes, an extra fee may be asked for.

When dealing with copyright, strive to stay above reproach, even if that means extra administrative time seeking permissions or having to cut a stellar song from your streaming.

If you're considering incorporating streaming into your services, check out these vendors:

- Brightcove.com

- Livestream.com

- Sermoncast.com

- Streamingchurch.tv

- TheChurchOnline.com

- Streamspot.com

- MyChurchWebsite.com

- UStream.com

Podcast Services and/or Teachings

Podcasting came into being in the early 2000s and is defined as a digital audio file that is made available on the Internet for download onto a computer or mobile device. Often, podcast series can be subscribed to for multiple installments. In other words, podcasts are a perfect medium for spoken-word recordings (sermons) delivered on a weekly basis.

Through iTunes or other podcast apps, offering a service podcast can be a valuable tool for regularly distributing messages to members who like to listen, or even watch, the message during the week. Members whose jobs have them traveling in their cars can listen as they drive. Stay-at-home parents or work-from-home members can have it on their TVs or computer monitors as they go through their day. And, assuming the podcast files and podcast app are set up correctly, the work of downloading a weekly podcast onto one's device is automatic. Podcasting is a nice, value-added feature for your church body. And, like streaming video, allows your church's teachings to be heard far outside of its walls and for many, many years into the future.

Use Social Media Wisely

Social media didn't exist twenty years ago. Now it's become such an integral part of our online lives that it cannot be ignored. Of today's major social networks, Facebook has taken its place as the granddaddy of all social media. Today, every church is almost expected not only to have a website but a Facebook page as well. While a church website provides information, a church's Facebook page can reveal a church's pulse. Some churches also use Twitter for quick announcements or Instagram for pictures of events.

Not all churches can spend a lot of time cultivating their Facebook connection simply because of manpower. Smaller churches are often limited with time and resources. As a compromise, some small churches have opted for their Facebook page to be their main church page, saving themselves the budget dollars of creating a pricey website.

There's no right or wrong solution here. The main thing is to ensure you have an Internet presence somewhere, and that the information there is current.

Social media posts can be quite fun for churches. When praise team members rehearsing for the weekend take a picture, post it with tags of the other team members, and express excitement for the upcoming worship service, this only helps build anticipation for the service! Or, when someone uses Facebook Live during a service, it shows those who couldn't be there that day (or who attend other churches) what's happening at your church in real-time. It also shows those friends of yours who may not even attend church that something cool is happening. Maybe they see a shot of the stage with the worship leader singing and the multicolored lights shining through the haze, with the electric guitar and drums jamming in the background, and say, "Hey! This is not my mother's church! Maybe I should check it out!" Social media can help your church get itself in front of other people, Christian and non-Christian alike, and God can and will use that.

Plan Your Staging

What you can do with your stage depends on several factors. If your church has a more traditional stage with the pulpit built in the middle, an organ on one side, a piano on the other, and the choir loft in the back, you're limited by what you can accomplish every week aside from new wall banners or colored lighting.

If your stage is more contemporary and most every part is movable, then your options are wide open. You can consider building stage sets or using more creative lighting. If your pastor uses thematic sermon series, which most do these days, you can plan stage sets according to the series. Ideally, you'll plan the stage sets and the supporting graphics at the same time. In reality, it rarely happens that way. Usually, creating the graphics happens first, and then those graphics are handed to set designers who strive to do the best they can with what they're given.

A stage designer or team then devises a set that will work practically and affordably and will match the color scheme of the graphics, fonts, etc. Sometimes, a "set" may just be projecting the designed graphic somewhere and using matching stage lights to highlight the imagery. On rare occasions, stage pieces may be thought of first, and those are fun times. However, that usually means the sets are going to require more preparation because they're usually grandiose ideas!

One important thing to remember when building stage props is that wood is heavy. Props onstage only have to appear to be what they are. They don't have to be what they are. If you want a cross that's ten feet tall, it doesn't have to be made of real wood. I've seen too many crosses this size made of real wood that weigh at least a hundred pounds. The secret to stage props is Styrofoam, or, as it's called in the professional world, EPS, which is short for the long name of Expanded Polystyrene Styrofoam. I've had to create fifteen-inch Roman columns about two-and-half-feet around with square bases on each end. Though they were easier to carry with two people because of their bulk, I could still carry them all by myself because we'd created them from EPS.

Finally, one of the coolest things about EPS is, if you find the right company, they can 3D scan nearly anything and then cut your EPS to match, at just about any scale. Once completed, their 3D re-creation will look like the original, minus paint. If you wish to paint it, you'll need to apply sealer first, let that dry, then paint. A quality artist can paint the prop to look like your original, and your stage prop will be so believable that your audience will never know the difference. Sealant and paint do add some weight to the prop, but an EPS prop is still quite a bit lighter than anything else that could be created. The only downside to EPS and such 3D computer scanning and carving is that it can get pricey. But if it's a prop you can use and re-use, the process and the cost are more than worth your investment.

Choose Tech for Your Needs, Not Your Wants

If you're a technical minister, you've likely been entrusted with a budget, a team, and maybe some volunteers. Above all, you've been entrusted with the heavy responsibility to ensure that technology is used to further the mission of your church and the overall mission of God on earth. That's why we always need to be aware of our calling. That's why we need to keep up with technological trends and the best resources we can use. That's why we need to help each other and hold each other accountable.

It's my hope that this chapter and every other word in this book have been helpful, and I pray that you continue to do the good work that God has called you to do.

IMAG, CHECKLISTS, ETC.
REVIEW QUESTIONS

1.   IMAG is an acronym for what?

   - Discuss the general rule of thumb as to when this becomes necessary in a large room.

2.   Discuss different philosophies on who IMAG is shot for and why it may be shot different ways in different venues.

3.   How well does your team your plan your worship orders? Do you plan the week of or several weeks out?

   - Discuss how this can be done better and why. Can this over-thought?

4.   What creative elements do you incorporate into your services? Where do you find your ideas?

   - What is your process for deciding which to actually use?

5.   Does your church utilize live streaming?

   - What successes and struggles have you had?

CHAPTER 13

Planning for the Future

Thi s chapter makes a feeble attempt to accomplish the seemingly impossible: predict the future. Only the prophets in the Bible have ever done this with true success. Here is one incredible example:

> *He was despised and rejected by men,*
> *a man of sorrows and acquainted with grief;*
> *and as one from whom men hide their faces*
> *he was despised, and we esteemed him not.*
> *Surely he has borne our griefs*
> *and carried our sorrows;*
> *yet we esteemed him stricken,*
> *smitten by God, and afflicted.*
> *But he was pierced for our transgressions;*
> *he was crushed for our iniquities;*
> *upon him was the chastisement*
> *that brought us peace,*
> *and with his wounds we are healed.*
> *Isaiah 53:3-5*

The Bible's prophetic success rate is second to none for one reason alone: God.

There's nothing he doesn't already know. Somehow, in his supreme, omnipotent way, he lives outside the confines of space and time. In fact, he commands it. He sees the beginning and the end at the same point, as well as every point in between. How does he do that? If I knew, I'd have written an entirely different book! Maybe there's validity in nerdy Star-Trek-based theories like the nexus and the existence of the space–time continuum, but who really knows God's power over time and space? Not me. Only God can predict the future. The rest of us just make educated guesses.

Actually, we just guess, and we like to think they're educated. So, these are my best guesses for what's just around the bend in technical ministry.

"I need a list of specific unknown problems
that we'll encounter."

*Image licensed through Stockphotos.com by Marty Hill and Quaddot Productions.
Used by Permission.*

Churches Will Replace Their Projectors With LED Walls.

Based on real technology already available, LED walls are becoming commonplace. Prices are still quite high, but prices are falling since LED lamps are becoming the norm, not only in theaters but in homes as well. As LED lamps decrease in cost, the cost of an LED wall will likewise lessen, even to the point where traditional bulb projectors may become uncommon if not obsolete.

The benefits of converting to LED walls are many: LED walls are much brighter than today's projectors. No shadows are cast on the wall since the light emits from the wall instead of onto the wall. LED walls use about 50 percent less power than their projector counterparts. LED walls don't require replacing expensive bulbs on a consistent basis, and their light intensity doesn't fade over time. Lastly, if a technical issue arises, fixing an LED wall often means just replacing one modular unit versus conducting an expensive repair on the whole unit of a projector.

Laser Projectors

In the meantime, most of the rest of us still have to content with projectors and the many different types of those that there are, with new technologies arriving everyday it seems. Old LCD still hangs around because they are cheap, but DLP and LED are still very common. However, laser projectors have come onto the scene and have become more affordable.

This really isn't looking into the future as much as is it a peak of what is out there right now for you. Laser projectors have two features that set them apart beside price:

Almost instant picture upon power up

Incredibly long life for the lasers as compared to lamps in regular projectors (20,000 hrs vs 1000hrs typically)

Image licensed through Stockphotos.com by Marty Hill and Quaddot Productions.
Used by Permission.

OLED-Based Screens Will Vastly Expand How Screens Can Be Used.

"OLED" stands for "Organic Light Emitting Diode." It's not a widely known term yet, but it will be in the coming years, especially in regard to smartphones, tablets, and other mobile devices. OLED displays use organic materials that glow a specific color when an electric current is applied. Individual pixels can even be completely shut down to achieve absolute black.

Because OLEDs are smaller and thinner than previous diodes, they can be harnessed to produce extremely high-resolution images. But what's more fascinating and helpful than that is that their size and adaptability can be incorporated into bendable displays. Such literal flexibility opens up all kinds of new possibilities for digital signage, creative stage design, or wherever your creative juices may take you. In the coming years, keep your eyes and ears open for OLEDs being incorporated into smartphones, TVs, monitors, and a whole host of devices that haven't even been created yet.

Virtual Reality And Augmented Reality Will Go Mainstream.

When Google Glass was announced in 2012, I hoped it would take off and quickly go mainstream. Google Glass presented augmented reality through a pair of software-enabled glasses. As a tech team leader, I saw how I hoped this technology would progress. The ability to always have certain vital information about the service right before my eyes seemed like a great idea. I envisioned it connecting to Planning Center Live, a robust, cloud-based piece of software for planning worship services. I thought how awesome it would be if I could always have the service order and the service clock right before, as well as some other communications system. No doubt, it would have taken some getting used to, but I felt it could become a valuable tool.

Hopefully, Google Glass will be resurrected or another company will create something similar that could offer helpful augmented reality. We are rapidly approaching an era where such devices will be released to wide acclaim. Even now, virtual reality hardware like the Oculus Rift, the Samsung Gear VR, the PlayStation VR, the HTC Vive, and Microsoft's Hololens are being heavily marketed to the general public. Technical ministers should consider how such devices may be used to further their work.

3-D video

3-D video becomes common—and watchable without 3-D glasses.

Although 3-D video has been around for a while, it's greatly matured over the last ten years, especially in the mainstream film industry. Most big-budget releases have a 3-D version. Even in the consumer and pro-sumer industries, 3-D cameras have become much easier to afford. So, why aren't our churches using 3-D video?

Admittedly, I've wanted to try creating a 3-D sermon illustration video for a long time, but I haven't had the resources—or the right kind of video—to justify the time and expense. I believe that shooting and using a 3-D video lends itself to specific videos. The 3-D effect would have to be purposeful in relation to the video and not just something done for its coolness factor alone. In other words, I wouldn't film one just because I could.

However, its newness and uniqueness could add a bit of spice to promos for Vacation Bible School or the next youth ministry retreat. I could also envision it being very useful for placing your congregation in the middle of Jerusalem or some other relevant location if a particular sermon illustration calls for it. Of course, you wouldn't want to overuse these kinds of videos. Figuring out the cost and distribution of those pesky 3-D glasses would often be a downside. But, with some creative, forward thinking, even that can be overcome. So, press forward in the meantime until the day of 3-D video without glasses becomes a reality!

A Social Media Platform That Doesn't End In "Book" Will Become The Largest Social Media Platform.

Well, this one might be fifty-fifty. Facebook is so large now that it would take a massive exodus to another platform for the social networking behemoth to relinquish its crown as the preferred online destination for more than a billion people as of late 2016 . But Snapchat, which Facebook tried to buy for 3 billion dollars in 2013 , might be poised as the "next new thing" that all the kids want to be on because their parents aren't.

So, what does this have to do with technical ministry? In our tech-laden world, the only constant is change. In the late 90s, I predicted that church websites would become our central hub of communication and replace so much of the printed material we once produced. I was mostly right. The printed church newsletter is a dying breed, and churches rely on their websites for much these days.

Both church members and the public rely on church websites for contact information, event announcements and registration forms, and streaming media for the church's sermons. Church websites also allow people to research multiple churches from the comfort of their own homes without having to drive to multiple addresses on multiple Sundays to try to find a suitable church home. The church website isn't going anywhere anytime soon.

But I'm not sure anyone anticipated the meteoric rise of social media and how quickly it became such a dominant communications medium of our day. Unlike staid and impersonal websites, social media platforms offer up-to-the-minute and personal communications. Event announcements and reports, as well as interactions between staff and members, member-to-member, and members-to-public can all take place on social media. These interactions may then provide a more transparent glimpse into the life of the church.

Some churches have even sought to incorporate social media into their worship services. For instance, local polling of a congregation is already used on occasion, and this ability to obtain real-time feedback may be used more in the future. To me, polling seems like a great way to engage a congregation—especially one that may already be looking at their phones.

Technical ministers would do well always to be on top of "the next big thing" when it comes to social media. Once you hear that most your congregation may be virtually congregating on a particular social network, that may be the time for you to finally step in and create an online presence for your church on that network. But always remember: what works on one social network seldom works on another. Learn the network, then leverage its benefits wisely.

Wireless Networking Will Become Ubiquitous.

Wi-Fi is the invisible backbone of nearly everything we do as technical ministers. Just pause for a moment and consider what would happen at your next Sunday service if your Wi-Fi signal isn't working. I shudder at the thought.

Wi-Fi allows our floor manager to cue talent to go on stage at the right time, for that talent to use a tablet with lyrics, and for me to simultaneously monitor ProPresenter, Planning Center Live, and our wireless mics status. And that's just a basic Sunday morning. If our Wi-Fi went down, I imagine we'd have to find an old-school projector and print some transparencies.

As we move into the future, wireless networks should get smarter, faster, more reliable, and more secure, so much so that we will totally forget that they're even there. And, maybe, gone will be the day that we have to find a new Wi-Fi network when entering a new building or new environment. Our devices will just know to connect, or they'll always be connected to a massive Wi-Fi network. We're not exactly there today, but the future is bright and beaming with clear signals!

Technology Will Reshape The World In Ways We Can't Imagine.

As technical ministers, we must always be learning. Even if a new technological advancement doesn't have a direct application to our work, we should still learn enough to be conversant about it. Plus, I'm fairly certain you're already wired that way. New tech is enticing and exciting, and part of our job is to know what's coming around the bend so we can properly vet its possible role in our churches.

For instance, self-driving cars are already a reality. Soon enough, they may even be picking us up and dropping us off—no driver necessary. If such a reality really takes off, what does that mean for our sometimes massive church parking lots?

As our homes become smarter and more connected—think Amazon's Alexa or Google's Home smart speakers—how can the church use such devices to encourage and inform members at home?

As medical advances continue to increase at an incredible rate and cause us to live longer, how does that affect ministry to every age group?

But the world sometimes gets stranger with technical advances, which raises questions such as what is the biblical mandate about video tattoos?

And how long do we have to wait for wireless electricity to go mainstream so that I never have to change another nine-volt battery in a wireless mic? (That day can't come soon enough.)

And when will I be able to enable a force field around myself in the sound booth when something goes wrong during a service? No lie: multiple companies are currently working on creating force fields. By using ultrasonic waves, one company hopes to create a force field around your windshield so that the bugs will slide right off or do not even hit it to begin with! This would be especially useful when driving through the Texas panhandle. Every time I've made that drive from Amarillo through Dalhart and into New Mexico my car has looked like I drove through a bug blizzard!

We live in a crazy world, and I believe it will just get crazier. But that's part of the fun.

As Christ spoke in parables, the primary communication medium of his day, so too must we use technology, the primary presentational tool of our day. Admit it or not, we are in competition with the secular world's presentational tools. They use technology to the fullest. They have larger budgets, more people, bigger venues, etc. While we will never win a technology contest—and we don't want that to be our goal— we need to at least try to speak to the masses where they are, sitting squarely in a technology-saturated culture.

We will always have something new to learn. We will always have something new to try. We cannot sit still for a moment. (Satan and his lowly minions aren't.) No matter your age, you can be proactive, diligent, forward-thinking, and innovative in your approach to what the future will bring. Always search and research what's to come. Always look for new and exciting ways to present the gospel so that more people might find the one thing they really need: Christ in their lives.

PLANNING FOR THE FUTURE

REVIEW QUESTIONS

1. What are four main things we need to know about a ministry job before we begin filling with staff or volunteers?

2. Discuss the different types of screen technologies and advantages and disadvantages of each:

   - Projectors:

   - LCD

   - LED

   - DLP

   - Laser

   - LED Wall

   - OLED Walls

3. How do the social media apps play a part in your church?

   - In your ministry?

   - What tools do you use to plan you services and schedule your teams?

   - Do they meet your expectations?

   - How could they do better?

4.   Discuss how you feel about always having to learn technologies, terminologies, etc.

   • How do you approach it?

   • Are you an instruction manual reader or a push-button-let's-see-what-this-does and learn as you go person?

   • Maybe you are a person who prefers to watch You-Tube tutorials instead.

5.   What things do you see for the future?

   • How can you plan for them?

   • Are you excited or nervous about it?

SO WHAT IS NEXT?

Alot has been written on how to lead a ministry. There has also been a lot written on the different aspects of technical ministry. Some of them are covered in this book, technical things like IMAG, video, live streaming, as well as mechanics because that is where a lot of the focus is these days.

We covered looking ahead to the future to predict what is coming so we can expand the methods of how we take the Gospel to the unreached masses of the world. We also want to reach those who have heard but have not yet accepted, hoping that in hearing the word in a new, cool technological ways that their eyes and hearts will be opened and another soul is won for the Lord. However, the future is always just that, and right when we catch up to yesterday's tomorrow, today will more times than not differ from we thought it would be. Today has its future we are trying to anticipate. It is always ahead of us. Always changing. Always uncertain. But we try to make our educated guesses to do the best we can and use resources in our ministries to the utmost of our abilities to further the kingdom on earth according to the great commission.

The next great thing to do with your ministry might be why you have been reading this book It is why I wrote it. Well the answer is always inside your own research for your own ministry needs. There are so many possible technology possibilities these days there is no clear direction you can or should go. Your ministry needs and budget are what would dictate what is next for your ministry. That is why no two churches are the same these days. There are many that are similar in lots of ways, but after the basics, there are many ways of doing just about everything. And there is no right or wrong. Whatever works for you and your church is the right way, whether it is in video, lighting, digital signage, Internet presence, or some other area.

But more than all of that, we covered what really matters the most. We covered the heart of the ministry leader: you. Before any hardware is turned on, before any camera is manned, before any light is brought up, the most important thing is the heart of the leader. It all starts there.

My entire thought process as I wrote was to produce content to help technical ministry leaders who had already started their ministries some time back take their next step. They would have a certain amount of technology and volunteer teams in place. Like myself, you probably had even attended conferences looking for new ideas, only to find breakout sessions were still basic. This book was to produce just that.

But the more I worked on this book the more the technical side of our ministry seemed to become less the focus. Instead, as all ministries should be, it turned to the Lord and how we approach Him through our service. It became more about leading those who serve with us so we may help others worship in new and creative ways. The technology is not the ministry. It is the tool we use. We must not succumb to our lust for the coolest and latest things in keeping up with the Jones' and we also must be certain we are not worshiping the creation, but the creator.

> People buy into the leader before they buy into the vision.[18] —John Maxwell

So, here we are. Asking what is next. You've even bought and read this book asking that question.

The answer is riddled in the next two questions...

- What does your ministry need?

- Where is it going? (every ministry is different.)

Remember the keyword is "ministry." If you are using the word "department" I challenge you to rethink that. Every area of a church is a ministry. Everyone in a church is a minister.

> *"...you yourselves like living stones are being built up as a spiritual house, to be a holy priesthood, to offer*

---

18   http://www.johnmaxwell.com/blog/teamwork-and-vision-go-hand-in-hand

spiritual sacrifices acceptable to God through Jesus Christ."

1 Peter 2:5

I encourage you to go forward with excitement with what the Lord will do through you and your ministry. With this I leave you with these closing verses of Ephesians 3:

For this reason I bow my knees before the Father, from whom every family in heaven and on earth is named, that according to the riches of his glory he may grant you to be strengthened with power through his Spirit in your inner being, so that Christ may dwell in your hearts through faith—that you, being rooted and grounded in love, may have strength to comprehend with all the saints what is the breadth and length and height and depth, and to know the love of Christ that surpasses knowledge, that you may be filled with all the fullness of God.

Now to him who is able to do far more abundantly than all that we ask or think, according to the power at work within us, to him be glory in the church and in Christ Jesus throughout all generations, forever and ever. Amen.

Ephesians 3:17-21

RESOURCES

JOB DESCRIPTIONS

This is a more complete list from the earlier chapter. While other positions exist in some ministries, this list covers the most common positions in use today. The detail job descriptions can be found as a free download-able PDF file at the following link:

http://www.quaddot.net/EGTTM_Resources/EG_JOB_DESCRIPTIONS.pdf

1. Producer

2. Assistant Producer

3. Technical Director

4. Video Director

5. Shading Operator

6. Camera Operator

7.   Graphics Operator

8.   Lighting Director

9.   Lighting Operator

10.   Audio Director (A1)

11.   Audio Assistant (A2)

12.   Broadcast Manager

13.   Broadcast Audio Engineer

14.   Stage Manager

15.   Assistant Stage Manager

16.   Grip

17.   Floor Manager

18.   Service Tech

19.   Communications Tech

20.   Minister Assistant

CHECKLISTS

These are examples of checklists that may inspire how you can use these. These are intended as starting points for you. Checklists are always living documents and you will find as you create you own they will grow and change over time, as these have.

Producers Weekly Checklist

http://www.quaddot.net/EGTTM_Resources/Producers_
Weekly_Checklist.pdf

ProPresenter Checklist

> http://www.quaddot.net/EGTTM_Resources/
> ProPresenter_Checklist1.pdf

Stage Manager Checklist

> http://www.quaddot.net/EGTTM_Resources/
> STAGE_MANAGER_CHECKLIST.pdf

Video Switcher Checklist

> http://www.quaddot.net/EGTTM_Resources/
> Video_Switcher_Checklist.pdf

Camera Operator Checklist

These are just a few suggested resources that might prove useful to you as you strive to advance your technical ministry to new heights. These are here at my discretion and are by no means paid advertising. I challenge you to be creative and innovative. Think outside the box.

Since these are sources outside my realm of control, I make no guarantees to the content in any form or fashion, nor that they will still be available when you go to find them. You can easily find more online with a little diligence in some fairly simple Google searches.

NETWORKING

Church Technical Leaders

http://churchtechleaders.org, https://ctl.onthecity.org

ChurchMedia.net

http://www.churchmedia.net

MOTION BACKGROUNDS

Digital Juice - digitaljuice.com

Triplewide Media - triplewidemedia.com

Motion Worship - motionworship.com

VIDEO HELP LINKS

Video connector fittings

- https://www.youtube.com/watch?v=nKEvciE5G7c

- https://www.youtube.com/watch?v=iQngGKrUqAo

Understanding Video Test Charts

- https://www.bhphotovideo.com/explora/video/tips-and-solutions/understanding-video-test-charts

- https://www.videouniversity.com/articles/color-bars-and-how-to-use-em/

Setting the Back Focus on a Camera

- http://nofilmschool.com/2011/12/set-backfocus-video-camera

Reading Waveform and Vectorscopes

- http://www.larryjordan.biz/technique-how-to-read-scopes/

- https://library.creativecow.net/gleissenber_tobias/premiere_pro_advanced_color_correction/1

AUDIO HELP LINKS

Understanding DB Meters

- http://www.explainthatstuff.com/soundlevelmeters.html

- http://www.prosoundweb.com/topics/audio/sound_level_meters_the_primer_what_how_why_techniques_more/

- https://www.av-iq.com/avcat/images/documents/pdfs/measdigaudlvls.pdf

Understand A and C Scales on Audio Meters

- http://www.hearforever.org/tools-to-learn/sound-source-a-and-c-weighted-noise-measurements

Audio Compression

- http://www.uaudio.com/blog/audio-compression-basics/

- https://music.tutsplus.com/tutorials/5-compression-techniques-and-how-to-use-them--audio-10322

- https://theproaudiofiles.com/compression-techniques/

EQ

- http://blog.dubspot.com/audio-equalizer-guide/

- https://www.howtogeek.com/59467/htg-explains-what-is-an-equalizer-and-how-does-it-work/

LIGHTING HELP LINKS

Cleaning Stage Lights

- https://www.learnstagelighting.com/how-do-i-clean-my-stage-lights/

Annual Maintenance

- http://www.pnta.com/customer-service/faq/lighting-maintenance/

MISC. HELP LINKS

How to Properly Roll Cables

- https://www.youtube.com/watch?v=0yPcJD7RVuY

Special Event Forms

- http://www.quaddot.net/EGTTM_Resources/special_event_forms.pdf

MARTY HILL

Marty Hill has been in full-time technical ministry since 1995, but has been around ministry for most of his entire life. Having grown up in the church, being saved in 1967, he got his music degree to become a band director from the North Texas State University, now the University of North Texas, in 1980. He and his wife, Lavonne, married in 1982 and have three children and two grandchildren at the time of this writing.

Marty has been on the technical side of ministry of several churches, having titles of media director, technical director and producer, leading teams of full-time and part-time staff and large teams of volunteers, where he says gets his greatest joy. He has also been involved in ministry by singing, playing several instruments, including trombone, piano or keys, and as orchestra conductor, choir director and worship leader.

He has produced a great number of videos for worship and has been contracted for freelance work by several companies. Beyond video, he is also music composer and arranger, going back on his music degree roots. He says he has seen God do many things, and that his faith grows daily, adding that when people asks for his testimony, he has to ask, "Which one?"

Check out Marty Hill's videos under Quaddot Productions, at Sermonspice.com.

COMING SOON

- More books from Marty Hill, including a more in-depth look at volunteer recruiting and management as well as personal growth.

- Continuing new video releases on sermonspice.com

- And other creative endeavors to expand the kingdom!

- Watch his website at Marty-Hill.com, QUADDOT.NET and QDPRO.COM.

Marty is available for conferences and consulting.

He can be contacted at:

Marty@qdpro.com

INDEX

Final Draft
  153
flaunt
  11, 20, 24
flesh
  32
footage
  164-165
forgiveness
  12, 33, 37, 151
forms
  56, 103, 107, 110, 223
foundation
  14, 98, 105
foundational
  11

G

gifts
  31, 33, 92, 101, 105, 130-131
GIGO
  68
gossip
  39, 165
grace
  13, 51, 57
graphics
  16, 55, 124, 139, 154, 184-185,
  187, 202-204, 208, 212, 236
growth
  32, 207, 243

H

Handling Exits
  122, 129
hardware
  171, 173, 179, 184-185, 221,
  232
harvest
  86
health
  70-72, 80, 127, 138, 141

Hebrews
  29
history
  12, 102, 111, 148, 199, 202
Hollywood
  66, 136
host
  107, 197-198, 220
humility
  2, 7, 12-14, 16-20, 26, 40, 43,
  58, 101, 103, 114-115, 118,
  127, 174, 179
husband
  62, 64

I

identify
  29, 31, 81, 146
ignorance
  7-8
IMAG
  2, 55, 139, 182-187, 191, 215,
  231
inexperience
  8
innovator
  3
insecure
  31-34, 36-38, 40, 42
insecurely
  31
inspire
  117, 145, 236
instrumental
  9, 12, 72, 189

J

job descriptions
  2, 107, 130-134, 136, 141-142,
  235

O

oblivious
32, 46
onboard
110, 121
open house
106-107
opportunities
42, 97, 114

P

pastor
14, 18, 29, 31-35, 37-38, 42,
46, 48-49, 52, 87, 93, 115, 128,
137, 139, 146, 155-156, 165,
187, 189-190, 198, 207, 212
pastors
2, 27-28, 31, 35-36, 46-48, 69,
76, 147-148, 165
pilot
168, 170, 180, 192
planning
2, 58, 60, 122, 138, 140, 158,
160, 173, 176, 178, 195-196,
199, 201, 216, 221, 225, 228
prayer
12, 53, 62, 86-89, 91, 105
pray without ceasing
87
preach
13, 29-30
pressures
29
pride
10-12, 14
principles
3, 27, 46, 78, 92, 99
priorities
78
Producer
135-140, 142, 197, 208, 235,
242

professional
11, 19-22, 24-26, 33, 37, 39,
62, 73, 76, 176, 180, 200, 213
projectors
175, 177, 182, 184, 218-219,
228

R

RAIDs
171
recommendations
14, 184, 192
recruit
85, 100, 103, 108-109, 111,
116, 132, 141
relationships
11, 15, 42, 80, 107
report
52, 56, 66, 201
resources
3, 20, 28-29, 41-42, 50-51, 53,
55-56, 59, 92, 134, 141, 154,
161, 165, 170, 191-193, 200,
202, 210, 214, 222, 231, 235,
237
respect
9, 11-12, 15-17, 28, 34-35, 44,
50, 67, 116, 122
responsibilities
65, 76, 85, 122, 129, 135, 137,
140
responsibility
8, 41, 64, 94, 123, 178, 213
righteousness
37
role model
35
rotation
112
router
175, 177
run sheets
195

Made in the USA
Columbia, SC
24 September 2017